SEX & LOVERS

SEX & LOVERS

A Practical Guide

Ann-Marlene Henning & Tina Bremer-Olszewski

with photographs by Heji Shin

CAMERON & HOLLIS

© 2014 Cameron & Hollis, PO Box 1, Moffat, DG10 9RU, Scotland
www.cameronbooks.co.uk

Originally published in German
by Rogner & Bernhard GmbH & Co. Verlags KG, Berlin

Translated, anglicised and edited by Cameron & Hollis
Replacement English graphics by Tom Seabrook
Typeset by Cameron & Hollis

German edition edited by Johanna von Rauch, Ida Thiemann
Layouts conceived and designed by Andreas Wellnitz

ISBN 978-0-906506-28-8

Printed and bound in Italy by Stampa Sud

CONTENTS

INTRODUCTION

WHO NEEDS SEX EDUCATION?

Nowadays it is easier than it has ever been to view and read about sex. References and allusions to sex are everywhere in the media, and the internet has made pornographic images and video available at the touch of a screen or keyboard. Strangely, though, most people are not much better informed about sexuality than previous generations were. Yet this relentless exposure to sex can easily make a person feel as though they've already seen everything and done it all. Unfortunately, sex as presented by the media has very little to do with reality. Long before they've ever kissed anyone, let alone slept with another person, a lot of young people have watched porn movies. And porn films are full of bizarre practices and misinformation. What they definitely do not show is real, fulfilling, genuinely shared sex.

In this book we want to talk about sex as it really is. That's why the photographs are such an important part of it: they show real couples having real sex, young people who care about each other actually sleeping together.

Our book has been written for young people who are just beginning to have sex or thinking of doing so. We start from the idea that everyone has an innate ability to become aroused, but that sexuality (and how to enjoy it) has to be learned. We want to encourage you to find out as much as you can about what goes on in your own body and how it feels, and to work out what your own preferences are and where your boundaries lie. Then you'll be equipped to discover the pleasure you can have with a healthy sexuality that's been defined by no-one but you.

Anyone can learn how to have good sex just as anyone can learn how to swim or ride on a skateboard.

The learning process begins much earlier than most people imagine. A child's first experience of arousal is likely to have been in the womb. To the amusement (or, occasionally, disgust) of his parents, ultrasound scans sometimes clearly show a male foetus having his first erection. It is, of course, harder to make out female arousal on a scan, but we now know that it happens.

For newborns, some of their very first sensual experiences happen when they are touched, squeezed, stroked, kissed. Every time a touch is felt, a sound heard, a change in temperature or breath of air registered, neural pathways are laid down in the brain, and then followed repeatedly. Memories of loving caresses are stored away, and gradually the baby learns to recognise them. This is how our personal inventory of sensual pleasure starts to be compiled; it's the beginning of appreciating a sense of well-being.

This is why it's a good thing, and important, for young children to discover and investigate their own genitals. Small children should be allowed to touch themselves freely and without constraint. As they find out how this feels, they will naturally develop a positive sense of their own sex organs. These early experiences will have a significant bearing on their future sex lives. Learning about sex begins very early on.

Many parents find it embarrassing when their children touch themselves or start playing doctors and nurses. When they feel this way, they are confusing their own sexual history with what the children are experiencing. The child is not aware of any sexual desire: he or she just knows what nice feelings one's own body can produce. It's not until much closer to adulthood that this kind of touching becomes linked to sexual awareness.

As a boy's genitals are on the outside of his body, they are clearly visible. He sees them every day and touches them when he urinates. When a boy goes for a wee with his dad or his friends, he does so standing up and, pretty much from the start, learns to take some pride in his penis.

It's different for girls. They pull their pants down, urinate, wipe themselves, pull their clothes up again, and they're done. This alone means that, from an early age, boys' and girls' levels of awareness of their respective sex organs are very different. That apart, however, neither girls nor boys know much at all about their own bodies or those of the opposite sex. These days, although a lot young people have heard about the G-spot and know about some fairly weird and unusual sexual practices, they often have very little knowledge of how their own bodies actually work.

Most girls grow up without ever having looked properly at their own genitals. Only a few will have had the kind of parents who were open enough to encourage them to use a mirror to take a look. Unfortunately, they're much more likely to have been told not to touch themselves, or even that 'there's nothing down there'. As a result, the female sex organs are shrouded in mystery, invisible and, in the opinion of too many adults, preferably never referred to.

That's why hardly any women have a name for their genitals that they feel comfortable with. The most commonly used term, vagina, actually refers only to the inner female genitalia. But people often use it when they're talking about the female sex organs in their entirety. The most visible, outer part of the female genitals is called the vulva – a name that sounds slightly comical and is more likely to make people think of Swedish cars than a part of a woman's body. That's why Charlotte Roche, among other female authors, has invented her own terms: in her book *Wetlands*, she calls the inner labia 'dewlaps', the outer labia 'ladyfingers' and the clitoris a 'pearl trunk'. Not a bad try.

You may well make up your own terminology, or pick up on names you've heard other people use. Here are a few examples of the vast range of slang names for female and male sex organs:

BAT CAVE, BEARDED OYSTER, BEAVER, BOX, CAVE, CHA-CHA, CHERRY, CHOOT, CLAM, COCK POCKET, COOTER, CUNNY, CUNT, FADGE, FANNY, FRONT BOTTOM, HOLE, HONEYPOT, KITTY, KOOCH, LADY FLOWER, LOVE CAVE, MEAT WALLET, MUFF, MUFFIN, POOKIE, THE PROMISED LAND, PUNANI, PURSE, PUSSY, QUIM, SLIT, SLOT MACHINE, SNATCH, TUNNEL OF LOVE, TWAT, TWITCHET, VADGE, WHISPERING EYE

BISHOP, CANDLE, CAPTAIN WINKY, COCK, DAGGER, DICK, DING-A-LING, DONG, DRAGON, DRUMSTICK, FERRET, HOSE, JACKHAMMER, JACK-IN-THE-BOX, JOYSTICK, KNOB, LITTLE SOLDIER, LONGFELLOW, MAGIC WAND, MUSHROOM TIP, ONE-EYED TROUSER SNAKE, PACKAGE, PECKER, PIECE, PORK SWORD, PRICK, PURPLE-HEADED WARRIOR, SAUSAGE, TOOL, WANG, WIENER, WILLY

TOUCHING

MASTURBATION & INTIMATE CARESSING

THAT FEELS SO GOOD

A dream has left you incredibly excited. Halfway between sleep and waking, you're cosy and warm under the bedclothes and feeling very, very sexy. Your fingers slip down between your legs: you start stroking, then pause, savouring the sensations you're creating. You may not quite know what is happening, then after a bit of friction, a bit of pressure, it happens. You come.

At some point between infancy and your teens it will have dawned on you that you can excite yourself. You may well have discovered this when you were very young, before you fully understood what was going on. Now you are really learning how to satisfy yourself. And it feels fantastic. Masturbating – jerking off, wanking, tossing off – is great. And the more you get to know yourself and your body, the better you become at manipulating your own excitement and fantasies. Now you're able to set off feelings and sensations that feel indescribably good.

Humans are hard-wired with the ability to pleasure themselves. Nature's intention is that we should all have as much sex as possible so as to perpetuate our species. But it takes some skill and practice to discover just what a rich experience sex can be and to learn how to build to a satisfying climax. So as to explain all of this more clearly, we need to provide you with a bit of scientific background.

In a newborn baby there are already many connections – or communication paths – established between nerve cells as a result of what has been sensed and experienced in the womb: touch, temperature and sound, for example. There are around 100 billion nerve cells in the brain, a single one of which can have more than 10,000 links to other nerve cells. These connections are responsible for our ability to experience sexual sensation and pleasure. Our bodies take a bit of time to become familiar with why and where they feel things, as neural pathways are gradually laid down.

This means that when we start masturbating we are creating our own individual routes to sexual pleasure and satisfaction. Imagine that you're learning to play the piano. You gradually improve until you can play a couple of simple tunes, and you're quite pleased with how they sound. Once you're able to use more than one finger at a time, you'll learn how to play in harmony. Masturbating is a bit like that. And, if you get together with another player, you can play fantastic pieces for four hands. If you want more from masturbation, there's much, much more to be had. So it's good to know how to get the best out of the body's keyboard, to learn how each body ticks.

Start, preferably on your own, by getting to know your whole body. Oils or body lotions are really good for this. Smooth some oil or

My first time I jacked off, I thought I'd invented it. I looked down at my sloppy handful of junk and thought, 'This is going to make me rich.'
Chuck Palahniuk

I had my first orgasm during third-grade recess . . . Obviously, I did not know why climbing that pole felt so wonderful, nor did I realise what I felt had anything to do with sex. I just liked it. A lot . . . Eventually I'd hit the precise spot and squeeze my thighs and pelvis as tight as I could while shimmying up and down a distance of three inches tops. And then I'd do it again. And again.
Anonymous online post

cream over your skin and concentrate on how this feels on different parts of your body. Don't leave anywhere out: arms, belly, legs, buttocks, then gradually get closer and closer to your more intimate parts. It isn't just the tip of the penis or clitoris that are sensitive to stroking. Touching the shaft of the penis, the testicles or the labia and all around the anus can also produce a lot of pleasure.

Find out how you smell and taste. Every human being has his or her own sexual fragrance, and everybody's is different. If you're male, try tasting a little of your semen. You'll discover that its flavour can vary according to what you've been eating. If you're female, use a finger to take a bit of the fluid from inside your vagina and taste it. You can also explore inside your vagina with your fingers and try to massage your hymen (but don't worry if you can't find it – a lot of girls have no trace of one, *see* page 126). The hymen is stretchy, and contrary to what a lot of people think, it always has an opening somewhere in it, and may have several, depending on the individual. If you can gently find a way through your hymen, you can even try feeling further up. You'll gradually get used to some very new sensations in places where you have never been touched before, and it'll help you to be more relaxed the first time a penis enters you.

Boys can try, while masturbating, to tilt their pelvis backwards and forwards, rather than moving their hand, which automatically moves the penis in a kind of thrusting motion. This will get you used to the kind of movement that you'll need to make if you start having sex with another person. You can even prepare yourself for the moistness of a vagina by using oil on your hand. If you're with a girlfriend, you can practise moving into her hand, and you can also use oil to stroke and gently rub her vulva. Find out what you both enjoy doing.

Feel free to use your imagination while masturbating. Work out which fantasies really get you going. Maybe you've seen pictures on the internet or in magazines that make you hot. Lie down in your bedroom or somewhere where you can be comfortable and won't be disturbed and let your thoughts drift, maybe making up stories or scenarios, if that feels good. And when you feel like touching your-self, go ahead.

Try experimenting, doing different things – like using more or less pressure alternately, varying the tempo of your hand or finger movements, or finding your own rhythm to move to. All kinds of movements can be done either fast or slowly. Varying the speed of touching can completely change how it feels. You can make small, exact movements or use the space around your body to make big, generous ones. If you make smooth, flowing movements with your pelvis when you're masturbating, you'll feel more than if the movements are short and jerky. Above all, give yourself enough time to let your thoughts wander and to savour your excitement. What you're concentrating on is not the orgasm itself, but the road towards it.

Don't knock masturbation. It's sex with someone you love.
Woody Allen

16

Physical tension, breathing, timing and movement all have their effects on the sensations you'll experience. Once you have learned to alternate between tensing yourself and relaxing, try out different rates of breathing, vary how fast you go, and the scope of your movements, and you'll be able to enjoy far broader and deeper levels of arousal. Rather than it being concentrated in one small area, you'll feel the excitement flowing through your whole body. All of this is a great way of preparing for sex with a partner.

Fancy trying something out? This arm experiment is really easy, and it can be done either with a partner or on your own. One of you sits on a chair, relaxed but upright. Place one arm on your thigh, then clench your fist and arm as strongly as you can, feeling the tension right up to your shoulder, and hold the position for a few minutes while your partner gently strokes your arm (or you stroke it yourself). The effect is to reduce the blood flow through your arm and hand. How does it feel? Now it's the turn of the other arm. But this time, allow the hand and arm to rest in a relaxed position on your thigh. Then stroke the arm (or ask your partner to do so). How does it feel this time? Any different?

You've probably discovered that the tensed arm was less sensitive and that you quite quickly got bored with being stroked. Maybe it even felt a bit unpleasant. In the relaxed arm, by contrast, you will probably have felt more, and the sensation may well have spread further. Men and women sometimes react slightly differently to this. As men usually have firmer, thicker skin than women, they're more likely to experience the stroking as tickling.

There's another trick you can do to intensify sensation. Taking slow deep breaths in and out while your relaxed arm is being stroked will allow the feelings to travel further through your body.

Finally, find out what happens if, while your arm is being stroked, you tense and relax your muscles alternately. This plus varying your breathing can make a big difference to the feelings you experience.

Now it's over to you. See if you notice whether having a bit more knowledge about what's going on has any effect on you when you are next masturbating.

Learning to masturbate is a bit like the stage before you learn to swim – you go through the motions on dry land and then you try them out in the water. So now you're on the brink of finding out more about this massive secret that seems to be such a big deal: sex.

Anyone who has practised on themselves has a clear advantage, because he or she already knows a bit about how their own body works and so can happily concentrate on another person. There's a lot about sex, whether you're on your own or with someone else, that just comes naturally. But sometimes it's no bad thing to get a few hints about how to make the experience even more rewarding.

The good thing about masturbation is that you don't have to get dressed up for it.
Truman Capote

A Short History of Masturbation

Anyone who masturbates already knows quite a lot about their own body and how to get excited. Fortunately, nowadays, most people have explored this a bit, but 100 years ago, masturbation was thought by many in Europe and North America to be dangerous and damaging. At the turn of the 19th and 20th centuries it was widely believed that masturbation could cause: exhaustion, irritability, dark circles under the eyes and a tendency to furious outbursts. In other times and cultures, masturbation was not frowned upon. In fact the reverse was true. In Ancient Greece, masturbation was regarded as a natural expression of normal sexual desire and a useful way of coping with sexual frustration. One of the gods revered in Ancient Egypt was believed to have created the universe by masturbating to ejaculation. In the Middle Ages, the Roman Catholic church regarded touching oneself in intimate places as a sin: so began the long, and sometimes vicious, campaign against so-called 'fornication'.

Well into the 19th century, masturbation was believed by many to be responsible for leprosy, cancer and a condition known as 'softening of the brain'. When they went to bed each night, children and young people were made to keep their hands on top of the covers or had their hands bound. And some poor children were even made to wear a kind of chastity belt to prevent them from fiddling with their private parts. A well-known supporter and proponent of these methods was Dr John Harvey Kellogg (1852-1943) who lived and worked in Michigan. Best known as the inventor of cornflakes (which he believed to be a useful dampener down of libido), Kellogg was a medical doctor who abominated sex, especially masturbation, and advocated removal of the foreskin in boys so as to make the glans less sensitive or threading a silver wire through the foreskin to prevent erections and cause irritation. For girls, he recommended the application of carbolic acid to the clitoris to reduce sensitivity. And all of this to prevent the young enjoying feelings of arousal.

The psychoanalyst Sigmund Freud (1856-1939) was one of the first to regard masturbation among children and young people as a positive thing. But it took a long time for the myths and negative opinions about it to fade away. For decades, people still believed that jerking off gave you spots or damaged your eyesight. Luckily, we now know that is total rubbish, although, even now, people tend to be more reticent when it comes to talking about masturbation than they are about regaling one another with tales of sex with a partner. Anyway, here's to the next climax!

BREATHLESS

A kiss. Hearts racing as lips move closer together. Explosions of colour behind closed eyelids. Unbelievable butterflies in the stomach. And then, the first delicate touch. Waves of heat flood your body like the warmth of a summer sun.

The mouth is slightly open, tongues hold back shyly . . . a brief pause, maybe . . . you look at each other and smile. And then you close your eyes once more, and your lips meet again. Kissing is the beginning of a conversation without words. You do something and the other person reacts. Two people can hardly come closer: when your lips touch, all distance between you is removed. That's why, for many people, kissing feels even more intimate than having sex. Small wonder that actors in porn movies mainly avoid kissing, and, if it's part of a scripted scene, they get it over with as fast as possible. It's not surprising, either, that most sex workers will have nothing to do with kissing. An intimate kiss, after all, binds love and sex together. And it isn't just a precursor to sex – it can be an end in itself. Think of the magical powers attributed to kisses in fairy tales. In real life, frogs don't turn into princes, but kissing can still transport you, intensifying and building desire. Kissing can be wonderful, so don't miss out on it. Even when you've been sleeping with someone for a long while, it can still be a wonderfully addictive pastime.

*How delicious is the winning
Of a kiss at love's beginning.*
Thomas Campbell

KISSING ETIQUETTE

Do: take your time, try gently nibbling, feel your way, take as long as you want, gradually build the intensity, bite gently

Don't: make your tongue as stiff as board**,** do too much licking**,** slobber, whirl and twist your tongue about in the other person's mouth.

ZACH But you said I could kiss you.
GABY Yes, my lips, not my oesophagus.
ZACH For your information, I've been told I'm a very good kisser, all right?
GABY By who? By the same girl who taught you to use your tongue like a windshield wiper?
Desperate Housewives

> **Mouth to mouth** When two people share an intimate, so-called 'French' kiss, at least 29 muscles are involved, including 17 in the tongue. They also exchange water, organic substances, fat, salt and hundreds of bacteria. Surveys reveal that around two-thirds of women would rather give up having sexual intercourse than do without kissing; the same is true of only about a third of men.

Our lips are among the most sensitive parts of the body. They react to the slightest touch. Kissing triggers nerve impulses that travel straight to the sex organs. The breathing rate speeds up, the pulse races, circulation increases, the excitement can be almost overwhelming. The truth is that intensive, intimate kissing sets off more bio-chemical

A kiss is something you need both hands for.
Mark Twain

processes in the body than sexual intercourse does. Kissing strengthens the immune system, because the exchange of bacteria prompts the production of immune cells (T lymphocytes), and the release of adrenaline and dopamine damps down pain and relieves stress. Best of all: serotonin and endorphins are released which produce exhilarating feelings of well-being and makes it easier for people to bond. It's estimated that people who kiss frequently may live as much as five years longer than non-kissers. And, even if you don't believe this, it's probably true that those who enjoy plenty of kissing have a nicer time than those who don't.

A kiss is a lovely trick designed by nature to stop speech when words become superfluous.
Ingrid Bergman

Kissing – who, why, when where? In its fourth month, a foetus in the womb can already suck its finger or thumb. Immediately after it is born, a baby feeds by sucking on its mother's breast. So the mouth is the most important point of physical contact between mother and baby. Kissing – it has been suggested – developed out of a feeding ritual: in many societies across human history mothers have chewed food (to break it down) before feeding it, by mouth, to their infants. Like breastfeeding, kiss-feeding creates a feeling of contentment and security, and the practice is now also thought to bring nutritional and immunological benefits for the baby. In some traditional cultures kiss-feeding still survives, and in 2012 the American actor Alicia Silverstone posted a controversial video on YouTube of herself kiss-feeding her 11-month-old baby son. But in general, in developed societies, kissing is used for greeting, saying goodbye, as a sign of affection, or as part of a ritual – as in the wedding ceremony. Other animals also use kissing as a sign of affection: chimpanzees, for example, kiss to signal forgiveness or reconciliation. There are some cultures in which kissing is not regarded as normal behaviour at all: in China, Japan and large parts of Africa, it is regarded as repulsive. In India, where it is considered disrespectful to display affection in public, films that show lovers kissing are still banned.

RELAX . . .

At the beginning of a relationship, just after you have got together, it's not easy to relax entirely or to let go of your inhibitions. And the first time you strip off and find yourself standing in front of someone else stark naked, you can end up feeling very nervous. Faced with the naked truth, or rather, true nakedness, the mere suspicion that you might not look perfect can produce the same level of alarm that you might feel before your first bungee jump.

I find flaws attractive. I find scars attractive.
Angelina Jolie

Blind Man's Buff Try switching the light off. Sometimes things go better in the dark, because you can really concentrate. You don't get distracted, and your senses tend to be more acute. Feeling, tasting, smelling, listening – everything seems a bit clearer and more intense.

Little by little, you'll get used to each other, and when you realise just how much you are arousing your partner, your inhibitions will simply disappear. And, seriously, do other people's zits or extra bit of weight bother you that much? Do they really get in the way of you enjoying yourselves? Quite the reverse: it's the tiny imperfections and variations that make each person special.

There's something sexy about a gut. Not a 400-pound beer gut, but a little paunch. I love that.
Sandra Bullock

THE JOY OF STROKING

Sexual togetherness usually begins with kissing, cuddling and stroking. The experience of intimacy can reach a whole new level with the use of just a few simple stroking techniques. Stroking is as much about how thoughtful you are being as it is about touching. Just making your partner feel that you are there entirely for them can make them very happy and is exciting in itself.

Here are a few suggestions of what you can bring to your caresses:

We'll call the lightest touch 'the butterfly'. The fingers dance lightly over the skin, like hundreds of butterflies landing and taking off again, flying high and brushing the skin with their wings.

'Drawing' involves slightly more pressure. The fingertips travel backwards and forwards over the skin as though drawing invisible lines – on your partner's arm or back, or wherever you like.

License my roving hands, and let them go Before, behind, between, above, below.
John Donne

Another thing you can do is to use your hand to 'see'. Let your fingers travel across the skin as though they want to investigate every tiny detail of your partner's body. They might pause at a mole and circle round it, or go round and round the elbow joint as if to find out where the bones lead. Sometimes the fingers might make circles, sometimes they might apply a bit of pressure as they get to know a particular area. There are certain parts of the body where this can be really erotic.

The most common way of touching is to allow the flat of your hand to glide over the other person's body. Most people know how to do that. Or you can use a kneading action, grasping your partner's body more decisively and applying more pressure, almost as if you are giving a massage. Lots of people enjoy being touched quite firmly round the shoulders, back, waist and hips. If you are feeling aroused and passionate, you'll probably automatically touch and hold your partner with greater urgency.

You can play around with these five styles of touching. It can be really exciting to alternate between them. You may find butterfly touches so amazing that they give you goose bumps, or they may be way too ticklish for you. Try to discover where your partner particularly enjoys being touched. If you're including the face, some people like having their lips touched and/or their face cupped in their partner's hands. Others particularly enjoy being touched on the nape of the neck and even, gently, on the throat. The entire body is an erogenous zone, and, unless you make the effort to explore it, much of it will will remain undiscovered.

INTIMACY DELUXE

After the first stage of cuddling, you're likely to feel more and more of an urge to take things further. There are no rules about when this should be. It could be after some weeks or months, or it might be only a couple of days – even just a few minutes. But when it happens, you'll be quite clear that you want more. What exactly would 'more' be, though? It definitely doesn't have to mean that you sleep together straight away. In fact, it's much more exciting to explore the intimate parts of someone else's body gradually, and to take it in turns to bring each other to climax. Make sure you enjoy this stage. It's often the best time of all, because everything is still so intense.

Take time to get to know your partner's body, and don't be too worried if either of you gets something wrong. Talk about what you both enjoy. Saying 'do that again, it feels great' will make your partner feel good and reassure them that they are on the right track. If your partner does something that you don't like, try to be tactful so as not to hurt their feelings, and suggest alternatives: 'If I'm honest, that doesn't do a lot for me, but I'd really like it if you could do this.'

Being aware of what the other person needs and wants is part of the secret of making things work, but a healthy dose of ego doesn't go amiss, and can be very sexy. If you are obviously excited, it's likely to make your partner even more aroused.

Follow your instincts and your heart and don't forget that you're meant to be having a good time.

I regret to say that we of the FBI are powerless to act in cases of oral-genital intimacy, unless it has in some way obstructed interstate commerce.
J. Edgar Hoover

Cool it! If you take things gently, you'll have a better chance of working out how your partner is reacting. Most people are not too keen on having their most intimate places felt up as if there's some sort of a tick list that has to be got through as efficiently as possible. Better to relax and enjoy some foreplay: touching or kissing on the mouth, the neck, the back, hips, thighs, or elsewhere.

HE LOVES ME, SHE LOVES ME NOT

Kissing, caressing, feeling hot – all of that has as much to do with emotions as with lust. So that you can navigate your way around all of this, it's worth knowing a bit about what happens in your brain and your body when it comes to sex and love. There are broadly speaking three states that you might find yourself in.

We'll start with good old-fashioned lust. This is when testosterone and oestrogen have kicked in – the hormones that are responsible for your sex drive and feelings of arousal. There's a huge yearning for sexual satisfaction. Whether or not your partner is the love of your life is irrelevant. You feel a pressing need to satisfy overwhelming desire.

Or you have fallen in love. In this case your choice of partner is very important. For the time being, you are utterly devoted to this particular individual. Now dopamine, noradrenalin and serotonin come into play: these are the happiness and feel-good hormones. You're on cloud nine, and don't want to let your beloved out of your sight. Unfortunately this stage does not last long. Our brains simply cannot withstand being lit up with hormones and constant sex for more than a short time. Apart from that, nature's intention is that each person should have a succession of partners so as to distribute genetic difference as widely as possible.

The very first moment I saw him, my heart was irrevocably gone.
Jane Austen

Finally, there are longstanding loving relationships. Our nesting instincts are governed by hormones called oxytocin (sometimes known as the 'cuddling hormone') and vasopressin, and these are involved in breastfeeding, touching, bonding, and orgasm, as well as having something to do with the times when you find yourself wanting to plan for the future and you're looking forward to maybe having children, and growing old together.

Everyone should be clear about which of these circumstances they find themselves in. Ask yourself whether you're looking for sex or love, a great one-night stand or a long-term relationship. Once you're clear about that for yourself, you can find out what the other person wants. At best, of course, you'll both be after the same thing. If your expectations start to diverge too much, you'll need to decide whether you should continue with the relationship or not. Of course, things can change. A one-night stand can turn into something more, falling in love can develop into deep, long-lasting love. Try to talk about these things together so that you can sort out whether what is happening is right for both of you.

When falling in love turns into a loving relationship, people's sex lives change too. Often, at the beginning, you can't get enough of each other. After you've been together for a while, though, you will notice – like most couples – that sex happens less often and may sometimes be less passionate. However, feelings of familiarity and security can

Each kiss a heart-quake.
Lord Byron

make this kind of sex deeply satisfying and enriching, even if it is a bit quieter.

Perhaps this is what the stories meant when they called somebody heartsick. Your heart and your stomach and your whole insides felt empty and hollow and aching.
Gabriel García Márquez

Broken Hearts Anyone who has been unhappy in love knows that the experience can be excruciatingly painful – more so than you could possibly have imagined. Brain researchers at the University of Michigan have discovered that the same areas of the brain react both to heartbreak and to physical pain. And it stands to reason: when a person is in love, the brain is flooded with feel-good 'drugs' or chemicals produced by the body, but when love goes wrong, those same chemicals are in short supply and you suffer from withdrawal symptoms. Time is the only healer. The first time this happens to you, it will feel as though the agony will never stop. But it will – honestly.

THE FIRST TIME

HERE GOES!

YES!

The first time you have sex, it may well feel stranger and more surprising than you were expecting. At some point, during a session of kissing or intimate caressing, you will have experienced sensations and feelings that were more powerful than anything you've felt before. Suddenly there's an overwhelming urge to go further, and you can't stop thinking about it. Your rational mind has very little to do with all of this. Your body is in charge now – instinct is taking over. Testosterone and dopamine are the hormones driving you, and they work like drugs. What you're experiencing is very similar to a drug high. Nothing else matters to you at this moment: you just want more, more, more ... And it's not easy to stop – which is why you both need to look out for each other, because right now contraception and protection could not be further from your minds. It's also why it makes a lot of sense to prepare for this moment in advance. The more clearly you've thought about your first time, the more likely it is to turn out as you want it to. Is it going to be in your own home, and are you just going to let things happen spontaneously? Do you want this to be a romantic occasion, or do you want to go wild? It may be some time before you work out exactly how you want to have sex. At some point, though, make sure both of you talk about it.

> I put my arms around him yes and drew him down to me so he could feel my breasts all perfume yes and his heart was going like mad and yes I said yes I will Yes.
> *James Joyce, Ulysses*

Starting a conversation of this kind can feel seriously daunting. It can be very hard to ask direct questions – 'Is this your first time? Have you slept with anyone before this? How was it? What protection do you use?' Or perhaps you're a girl and you're thinking of paying a visit to a sexual health clinic: 'Do you think I should ask about getting the pill?' You're not sure how the other person will react, and it's embarrassing. And if you're unlucky and start blushing, that makes it even worse. Even so, it's really good to get into the habit of talking about this stuff. After all, sex itself is a kind of conversation. And if someone refuses to discuss it, it probably means that they are even more anxious and unprepared than you are.

When you are both absolutely certain that you want to have sex, it's worth discussing exactly when you want to sleep together for the first time, what kind of protection you're going to use, and who is going to organise what. One of you might go to get contraceptive advice, for example, and the other might be responsible for buying some condoms. Deciding exactly where and how your first time is going to happen, and finding out what you both have in mind, are things it's good to talk about calmly and in advance.

> 'I'm a raging mass of hormones that I'm too young to understand,' said Bean. 'You're a female of a closely related species. According to all the best primatologists, I really have no choice.'
> 'That's nice,' she said.
> *Orson Scott Card, Shadow Puppets*

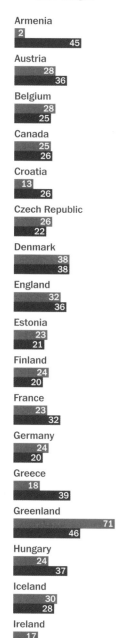

Armenia
2
45

Austria
28
36

Belgium
28
25

Canada
25
26

Croatia
13
26

Czech Republic
26
22

Denmark
38
38

England
32
36

Estonia
23
21

Finland
24
20

France
23
32

Germany
24
20

Greece
18
39

Greenland
71
46

Hungary
24
37

Iceland
30
28

Ireland
17
27

Love Hormones When you fall for someone, the object of your affections is never out of your thoughts. You want to be together day and night. When you're apart, you miss the other person desperately. And it's no wonder, because the hormones responsible for these feelings work just like drugs: that terrible longing has a lot in common with addiction.

Dopamine is a feel-good hormone. When dopamine levels rise, as they do when you're in love, you feel amazingly good. And when you're actually with your lover, the dopamine levels climb even higher: you're walking on air. By contrast, being apart can literally cause physical pain. That's why we are capable of doing crazy, sometimes ridiculous things when we're in love.

STOP IT!

There's a lot to deal with when you are learning about your own sexuality. Hormones unleash some really confusing feelings. Suddenly everything seems very intense and mixed-up, and it can all get too much. As if that isn't enough, different hormones come into play for boys and girls, and that creates even more confusion. You're coming to terms with a whole new set of feelings, and, at the same time, trying to work out what's happening to the opposite sex. Even someone you've always got on with really well and felt close to can suddenly seem like a stranger.

The main reason for this is that boys' levels of testosterone are now much higher: twenty times greater than in girls. Impatience, aggressive behaviour and feeling horny are all by-products of heightened levels of testosterone. The good news is that these levels stay pretty constant, so men are largely spared the hormonally induced mood swings that women have to cope with.

For girls it is more complicated. Progesterone and oestrogen arrive on the scene – both of which can have massive effects on mood. Levels go up and down at particular stages in the 28-day menstrual cycle (see pages 116-119), and are responsible for the mood swings a woman sometimes suffers. These can make for tense times both for her and for those around her. She might be moved to tears by the sight of a tiny kitten or become extremely irritated for no identifiable reason. This can make living together really hard and may put a lot of pressure on a relationship. It can also complicate your sex life.

Let's suppose, for example, that you've planned your first time for a particular weekend. He's gone to a lot of trouble: the bed has been freshly made, the candles are lit. At first, there's some foreplay. He is very tense. She is feeling extremely sensitive, because her hormone levels are dipping. He thinks everything is going pretty well. But suddenly she says, 'I can't do this. Stop!' He can't understand what's gone wrong. They had talked it all through beforehand, and now she's messing around. Doesn't she trust him? He feels bitter and disappointed. And she can't understand how he could be so insensitive . . . this is supposed to be about more than just sex. She is sad and disappointed.

That sounds like a recipe for falling out. But if you have some idea of what is happening in the other person's body, you'll be able to react with much more understanding.

Boys are, quite literally, under pressure, and sometimes it's very hard for them to break off in the middle of what they're doing. For this reason, it's good to say something as soon as you know that you don't want to go on. In any sexual relationship, both partners have the right to say no at any point. If it's not working, it's not working. Remember that you don't necessarily have to have sexual intercourse to enjoy great sex.

Sometimes you might not like what is happening or don't want it to continue, but can't quite manage to say so. Then it can be a good idea to let your body do the talking. You will, in any case, be drawing back automatically if you're not happy with what is going on – you won't be kissing with so much enthusiasm or joining in with what your partner is doing. You won't be holding the other person as you had been, or you might even have taken your hands away altogether. Guys on a testosterone high may well not even notice these signals, however obvious they seem to a girl. But whether you're a girl or a boy, if you ever feel bad about what is happening, you need to pause. Regroup, be brave, and say, clearly, that you want to stop.

Sometimes what girls want to do is just to go on and on caressing and kissing without taking things further. But that can be practically impossible for boys whose rapidly building excitement cannot be thrown into reverse. This is when there can easily be misunderstandings. He is thinking: *She really is up for it after all!* And she is thinking: *Why won't he give up on this? Can't he take a hint? I've already explained that I don't want to do this.* And then it's stalemate. There's only one thing for it: talk to each other!

Never try to get around your partner if he or she doesn't want what you're offering. No means no! If you keep asking: 'But why not?', it's likely to be counterproductive. You have to play fair: nobody should pressure anyone into doing anything against their will. Also, you shouldn't get someone excited and deliberately tease them, knowing that you don't want to follow through: that goes for both boys and girls. Think how a successful ice-skating duo behaves. The dancers are only any good if they can depend on each other and support each

Italy
22
26

Latvia
18
27

Lithuania
12
26

Luxembourg
24
37

Macedonia
3
31

Netherlands
22
19

Norway
30
26

Poland
13
19

Portugal
18
27

Romania
17
48

Russian Federation
18
37

Scotland
35
27

Slovakia
10
15

Slovenia
24
31

Spain
20
23

Sweden
32
31

Switzerland
16
23

Ukraine
17
40

Wales
39
29

other when something goes wrong for one of them. Both partners need to look out for each other and be aware of how the other is reacting. If one dancer forces the other to tackle too challenging a routine, the partner will falter, lose confidence and might even take a fall. Better to lead up gradually to new things. That way your partner's self-confidence and sense of security will grow. And you'll dance even more beautifully together.

Perhaps you're worried that you'll lose your girlfriend or boyfriend if you don't sleep together straight away. But if your friend really cares about you, there'll be no problem with waiting until you're ready. Sometimes, if you haven't yet had sexual intercourse, you can feel pressured by friends to 'go the whole way'. You should let this kind of advice go in one ear and out the other. Only you can decide when you're ready.

CAN I ASK YOU SOMETHING?

What a day, eh, Millhouse? The sun is out, birds are singing, bees are trying to have sex with them – as is my understanding . . .
Bart, in The Simpsons

You may find the idea of talking about sex to adults seriously embarrassing, and the thought of having conversations with your parents on the subject may make you cringe. But parents can be helpful in certain situations – when you need to decide what to do about contraception, for example. If talking to them really isn't possible, find another adult you can trust – an older sibling or relative, perhaps. Sometimes the advice of someone more experienced than you can be exactly what you need. But how best to approach talking to parents? That depends, first of all, on how they're likely to react.

Conservative parents believe that it is best to wait until you are married to have sex. This may come out of their religious beliefs or from strongly held moral convictions. (Unfairly, girls are more likely than boys to experience this attitude.) That is the hardest situation to cope with. Parents like these are likely to be evasive, dodging your questions by implying that you shouldn't even be thinking about such things. If you are up against this kind of opinion, it's best to approach someone else. Maybe you know another adult you can trust who will be able to answer your questions. If you'd prefer to remain anonymous, call or email a helpline. You'll find relevant contact details on pages 250-251.

Many parents are relieved if you bring up the subject first, because they find it so difficult to start a conversation about it themselves. They may be bit uptight, but still want to do the best they can to discuss things and come up with answers. With parents like these, you need to try to be as relaxed as possible. Be generous and understanding, and forgive them if they express themselves a bit awkwardly. It is, at least, worth a try. But if it doesn't work out, try talking to older brothers or sisters or other trustworthy adults.

Then there are open-minded parents. They will have been talking to their child since early childhood about sexuality and love, missing no opportunity to express their opinions on the subject. Parents like these are broad-minded and open. That's great in some ways, because you can go to them about anything, but it can also get on your nerves if they're always going on about it.

Many parents think that if young people talk about sex early, that automatically means that they are already having sexual intercourse. In fact, this is almost never the case, and the opposite is more likely to be true. A number of surveys in various countries have shown that the more informed a young person is, the later their first sexual experience tends to be. If your parents try to block conversations about sex because they think you're too young to have them, mention this to them.

In the end, though, no matter what kind of parents you have, it will almost always take a real effort to broach the subject of sex with them. If you're lucky, though, the conversations could turn out to be quite fun and interesting. What is certain is that they are a test of the maturity of the parent-child relationship. And who knows? Maybe your parents will learn something from you.

I hate it when adults use the term 'sexually active'. What does it even mean? Am I gonna like deactivate some day or is it a permanent state of being?
Juno

Who or what is your main source of information about sex?

Results as percentages of those questioned

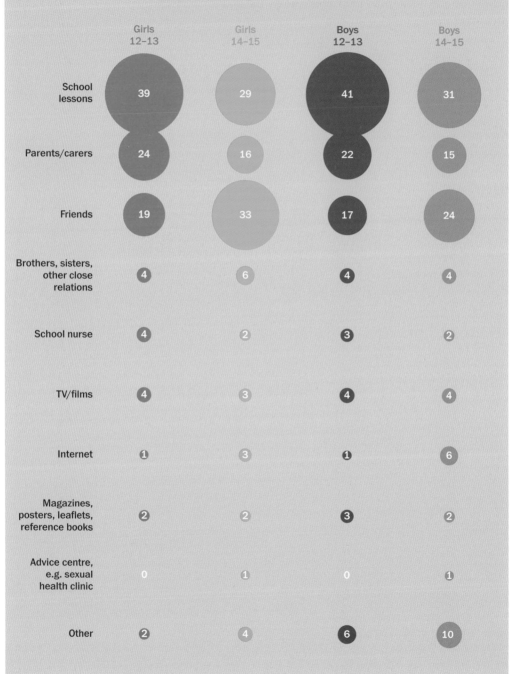

	Girls 12–13	Girls 14–15	Boys 12–13	Boys 14–15
School lessons	39	29	41	31
Parents/carers	24	16	22	15
Friends	19	33	17	24
Brothers, sisters, other close relations	4	6	4	4
School nurse	4	2	3	2
TV/films	4	3	4	4
Internet	1	3	1	6
Magazines, posters, leaflets, reference books	2	2	3	2
Advice centre, e.g. sexual health clinic	0	1	0	1
Other	2	4	6	10

Who would you prefer to be your main source of information about sex?

	Girls 12–13	Girls 14–15	Boys 12–13	Boys 14–15
Parents/carers	40	29	34	24
School lessons	28	28	32	28
Friends	12	17	11	17
Brothers, sisters, other close relations	4	6	4	5
School nurse	7	5	4	3
Advice centre, e.g. sexual health clinic	1	3	1	2
TV/films	1	2	3	4
Magazines, posters, leaflets, reference books	3	4	4	4
Doctor	1	1	2	3
Internet	1	2	2	8
Telephone helpline	1	1	1	1

From what age is it legal to have sex?

heterosexual

gay   lesbian

illegal

14 or 16

14 or 16   14 or 16

Austria, Germany, Portugal

16, or 14 if older partner is under 18

14

Togo

14

18   18

Chile

14 m or 16

14 or 16   14 or 16

Paraguay

14 if married, otherwise 16

15

15   15

**Czech Republi
Denmark, Fran
Iceland, Monac
Poland, Roman
Slovakia, Slover
Sweden, Urugu**

16

Algeria, Belize

lesbian sex unrecognised

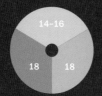

14–16

18   18

India

Age for heterosexual sex varies between states – in some cases younger than 14 if married.

16 and 19

18   18

Indonesia

16 for women, 19 for men

16

16

Jamaica, Namibia, Singapore, Sri Lanka, Uzbekistan

17

17   17

Ireland, Northern Ireland

18

18   18

Costa Rica, Dominican Republic, Guatemala, Haiti, Malta, Panama, Philippines, Rwanda, Thailand, Turkey, Vietnam

16 m or 18

Barbados

16 if married

18 m

Afghanistan, United Arab Emirates

only if married

18

**Bhutan, Burun
Eritrea, Tanzan**

13 13 13

Burkina Faso, South Korea

13

Nigeria

13–18 13–18 13–18

Japan

different ages in national and prefecturial law

14 14 14

Albania, Bulgaria, China, Columbia, Croatia, Ecuador, Estonia, Hungary, Italy, Liechtenstein, Lithuania, Montenegro, Peru, Puerto Rico, Serbia

15

Ethiopia

lesbian sex unrecognised

15

Morocco

16 16 16

Andora, Armenia, Australia, Azerbaijan, Belgium, Bosnia, Cambodia, Cuba, Finland, Georgia, Jordan, Luxembourg, Netherlands, New Zealand, Norway, Russia, South Africa, Spain, Switzerland, Taiwan, UK (excluding Northern Ireland), Ukraine, Venezuela

16 m

Bahrain

Heterosexual sex only if married, gay and lesbian sex unrecognised.

16

Ghana, Liberia

16 18 16

Bermuda

16 18 18

Bahamas

16 and 18 18 16

Canada

no anal sex before 18

18 18

Egypt, Kenya, Uganda

20

Tunisia

21 21 21

Madagascar

18 m or 21

Cameroon

18 if married

m

Iran, Oman, Pakistan, Qatar, Saudi Arabia, Sudan, Yemen

only if married

Age of Consent Most countries set the age of consent (the age at which it is legal to have sex) somewhere between the ages of 14 and 18 years old, although the lower limit can be as young as 12 (in Angola, for example) or as high as 21 (Bahrain). In the USA the age of consent ranges from 16 to 18 years old, depending on which state you are in. Canada has set the age at 16, as have the UK and New Zealand. In Australia, the age of consent is either 16 or 17, depending on the state or territory, and in Northern Ireland and the Irish Republic it is 17.

In the UK, the law covers everything from sexual touching to full intercourse, including masturbating together, and as in most European countries, the law is the same for both sexes, whether gay or straight. In Britain, a boy who has sex with a girl under 16 is breaking the law, even if she has agreed to it. If she's 13 to 15 years old, he could go to prison for two years. And the maximum sentence for having sex with a girl under 13 is life imprisonment. Once you're over 16, the law assumes that you are responsible for making your own decisions about who you have sex with, and there's no problem in having consensual sex – that is, sex that you have both agreed to – with someone older than you, unless your partner is in a 'position of trust' over you (this includes doctors, carers and teachers). It's illegal for anyone to have sex with under 18s in their care. Many countries, including North America, enforce similar conditions in their age of consent law. If you're going on holiday abroad, and you might have sex while you're away, make sure you know what is legal in the country you're visiting.

LOOK AND LEARN

We've already talked a bit about satisfying yourself. Once you and a partner start touching each other intimately, you will be finding out, as you go, what you both like doing or having done to you. It can be really arousing to ask your partner how he or she feels about what's happening. Some people are turned on by watching while the other person masturbates, and it can also give you some ideas to follow up on yourself. Of course, communicating about sex is not always easy. If you find it tricky, just leave it to your body to express what you feel: if you like something, smile or make contented noises, or stretch your body up against your partner's, or guide your partner's hand to touch you exactly as you like it. It works in the same way when you don't like something: if your partner is lying there motionless, not making a sound, it ought to cross your mind that all is possibly not well. You can gently ask what's going on, or try something different.

Sex is just another form of talk, where you act the words instead of saying them.
D.H. Lawrence, Lady Chatterley's Lover

If you can communicate about these things, it'll be almost like handing your partner an instruction manual, and it can make a big difference to how good the sex you have together can be. But if you act as though your partner is a mindreader, and don't explain clearly or show what you need and how you like to be touched, you'll probably be waiting a long time to get what you want. So, time to start talking! If you've tried having this kind of conversation, and your partner doesn't pick up on any of your suggestions or requests, then perhaps you need to ask whether you're with someone who is right for you.

PLEASE DON'T STOP!

Kissing, stroking, hands everywhere. Your heart races … you feel hot … your breathing speeds up … you feel more horny than ever before! You realise that today things are going to go further than foreplay. It's good that you're prepared, with condoms at the ready. Guys – at last it's happening, the moment you've been waiting for. Now all those hours of kissing and cuddling and caressing – and holding back! – are paying off. After some hot foreplay, you start allowing your fingers to approach the vagina. Slowly and gently, let your fingertips explore its entrance. (Short fingernails are a definite advantage here.) Keep an eye on your partner's face, watch her expression, and if she likes what you're doing, carry on. It's about now, if you're both ready, that it would be good to slip on a condom. If you have already practised doing this, so much the better. There's more information on page 212 about the best way to apply a condom.

One night of magic rush The start: a simple touch. The Knife, Heartbeats

The first time, you'll find the missionary position the easiest, because your girlfriend can lie there completely relaxed, and you can both have unbroken eye contact. So, she lies on her back in front of you, her legs spread, her knees up. You're above her, with your penis between her legs. To penetrate her, take your penis in your hand and try, very gently, pushing it in between her labia. You may well wonder whether it will go in. But don't worry, it doesn't matter what your penis looks like, what shape it is, the vagina will be able to stretch or contract to accommodate any size.

To begin with, you may feel some resistance, either because the labia, swollen with excitement, feel really thick, or because the hymen is barring the way. You can ask your partner to help guide your penis in. One of you can gently part the outer labia a little. Then try again, with really gentle thrusts, to enter her. You may find that so exciting that you come straight away. Don't get frustrated or moody – it happens to lots of people. If you say something like, 'I'm sorry – you just excite me so much that it's hard to control myself', it turns it

Yes. Good.Nibbling the earlobe. Kneading the buttocks, and so on, and so forth. So, we have all these possibilities before we stampede towards the clitoris, Watson. Monty Python

into a compliment. And, after a while, you can both try again. Or you may still have an erection, in which case try – as gently as possible – to enter her again. Keep in touch with your partner while all this is going on. Look at her, maybe talk to her ('Is that nice? Shall I go on?') and be aware of her body language.

Then, you can start to move slowly inside her – in whatever way pleases both of you. It's good to be cautious to start with. Pull out a little way and then push in again. Enjoy the feeling of being so close to her. Stay inside her without moving at all, or, when you're already in her, push a tiny bit deeper inside and move yourself around in all directions. This will result in less friction for you, so you'll be able to last longer. The slight pressure will also make her feel you more. This has nothing to do with the manic pumping in and out that you see in porn movies. When you're just starting to have sex, it's best to avoid experimenting with crazy positions which will just get you worried and upset. Be patient and loving, and everything else will come with time.

He felt now that he was not simply close to her, but that he did not know where he ended and she began.
Leo Tolstoy, Anna Karenina

AND NOW FOR THE GIRLS

It's really important that you are feeling good, and relaxed, because you are the one, who has, quite literally, to open herself to her partner. You're already excited, but now you're ready to go further. Many women describe an overwhelming desire to be 'filled'. If you get to this stage and your partner has already put on a condom, you can help him by taking his penis in your hand and guiding it towards your labia. Your outer labia are likely to be swollen with arousal, which can make it difficult for your partner to find the opening of your vagina. You can gently part your labia with your fingertips so that your friend can find the way in. A bit of moisture will help the penis to slip in more easily. If you're dry it can be unpleasant, because skin will be rubbing against skin, and the penis may push in with a sudden jerk.

When a penis enters you for the first time, you may feel a slight pain, but usually this will disappear pretty quickly. If the sensation is unpleasant, stop, and try again another time. It could be that, actually, you're not as ready as you thought you were, and your vaginal muscles have tensed, literally sealing you up. Or your friend may have been too energetic in his efforts to enter you. Maybe it's just the shock of discovering that something can get so deep inside your body. Savour the sensation of being filled up by him. Feel the connectedness between you. If he isn't particularly experienced, it's very likely that he'll come faster than you would like. Don't be disappointed that he has galloped on ahead of you – look forward to the next time.

Lovely and Moist . . . Whether or not you are noticeably moist the first time depends on how your hymen is formed. The hymen never seals off the entrance to the uterus completely, so moisture can trickle past it, even if you are a virgin. Extra moisture produced in the vagina is a direct result of you becoming excited. You can become aroused without even knowing how it happened – sometimes your body can be way ahead of your conscious thoughts. So you may find yourself getting moist even though sex hasn't crossed your mind. Sometimes the opposite can happen: you're definitely feeling sexy, but you're still dry. If you're stressed, or put yourself under any pressure, or if you're doubtful or afraid, your body can switch off, and then no moisture is produced. Dryness can also occur, though, if you are tensing your pelvic floor too much for too long. The vagina becomes wet more easily when it is not static – in other words, when it's massaged from the inside by the pelvic floor. A good tip for the first time is to use saliva or a lubricant (which you can buy at a pharmacy). But beware: if you're using a condom, make sure you get a silicone- or water-based lubricant; oily or greasy creams can react with the rubber causing the condom to develop tiny holes and even to tear.

When he withdraws his penis, make sure that he keeps a firm hold on the condom so that it doesn't come off and allow sperm into your vagina. If he doesn't do this, just hold on to it yourself, because you're also responsible for what's happening. Don't be shy!

Oh, and by the way, it is extremely rare for women, especially when they start having sex, to get an orgasm from the simple in-and-out movement of a penis. Achieving one has a lot to do with experience and technique. Sex scenes in romantic films or porn movies give the impression that women can come at the click of a finger. Like a lot of other things in these films, this is nonsense.

Both of you should follow your hearts, listen to your bodies, and concentrate on working out what you really want. And then do what is good for you.

PLEASE DON'T GO!

Now you're lying there, out of breath. At last it's happened. *I can still feel you on my skin.* She looks at him: his eyes are closed. *I do not believe it! Has he actually gone to sleep?*

It's often very different for men and women after sex. While it's happening, both are flooded with the hormone oxytocin and react similarly. But afterwards it can have different effects. Many people love snuggling up to their partner, cuddling, even talking – making the moment last. But others just want to keep to themselves, and need peace and quiet; they'll go straight to sleep. So if you're the one who is left lying awake, try not to feel resentful. This is just how it is sometimes, and it has nothing to do with whether someone likes you or not.

When you're arranging to see each other, make sure you've left enough time to be together afterwards. Don't just jump up as soon as you've finished and go out. Even if one of you has a short nap, you can still lie together for a while afterwards and go over what you really enjoyed and perhaps what you didn't like so much. Treat each other with care and love, because after sex you'll both be especially sensitive.

WAS THAT REALLY IT?

And this is supposed to be the most wonderful experience of all time? All that preparation, excitement, stress – just for that? The first time you have sex, your expectations are likely to be sky high, and the experience will almost certainly fall short of what you had hoped for. It may be over very fast. It may not be very romantic. The first time they have intercourse, most girls don't get anywhere near having an orgasm. Even so, this is a unique moment that you'll remember for the rest of your life, and it may well shape your future sexuality. The great thing is that the next time is likely to be better and the time after that even more enjoyable. On to the second round!

THE SECOND TIME

AND ALL THE OTHERS

WAS I OK?

So you've had sex for the first time, and then for the second time, and now you're launched. Everything is becoming more familiar, and you can relax a little and start noticing more about what is going on. There's a lot to explore. But it's often at this point that a mean little voice inside your head starts whispering: *So? How do you think you're really doing?* As soon as you've had sex for the first time – maybe even before that – you may well already be worrying about what kind of an impression you're making, how you're performing: *I want to be really good in bed ... I want her to go on fancying me for ever ... I want to be the only person he ever wants like this.*

This may sound weird or even unattractive, but actually it's quite understandable. If you're in a relationship with someone, you want to be able to prove that in every possible way, including sexually, you are the only right person for him or her.

Men tend to express these aspirations differently from women. Some see the whole thing as a test of athletic prowess. Others seem to have the impression that with a bit of training under their belts, they already belong to the Champions Sex League. A bit of nipple- and clitoris-rubbing here, a bit of licking there, followed by a long session of in-and-out, and wow, that was great sex!

So what does being good in bed really mean?

Lots of men think that for sex to be any good, the woman must have an orgasm, and they regard themselves as failing if their partner doesn't climax. As they see it, because most women take a while to reach orgasm, it's essential for men to be able to keep going for a long time. Of course it's a good thing to be thinking about your partner's orgasm. But what a lot of young men – and some older ones – don't realise is that for many women reaching a climax is not necessarily the most important thing.

It doesn't necessarily follow that having an orgasm equals great sex. Anyway, it's unrealistic to think that a woman will come merely as a result of a penis moving in and out of her. There are other kinds of movement that she will find far more arousing and pleasurable. If you take a look at the chapter on sexual technique, you'll find a lot more on this subject (see pages 147-165), including descriptions of positions that allow a man to keep going for longer. After all, a bit of staying power – when you want to change position, for example – does not go amiss.

If the man is absolutely determined that the woman must come, and concentrates exclusively on trying to make this happen, it can be very stressful. And because most women don't want to disappoint their man, some will even go to the lengths of faking it. So please

Promise me you'll never forget me because if I thought you would I'd never leave.
Winnie the Pooh

43

don't obsess about orgasms. It's not just about where you're going, it's how you get there.

Being good in bed means, above all, looking out both for yourself and for your partner, being happy to experiment and try things, and not being ashamed to say what you do and don't like.

Here are a couple of examples of scenarios that can happen only too easily. He is licking her, and all the while she is thinking: *This is really not my thing, but I'm going to let him go on doing it because he's enjoying himself so much.* Or she is rubbing his penis, and he is thinking, *I really wish she would grasp it more firmly*, but he doesn't dare say so. Neither of them is giving their partner a chance to do any better. Misunderstandings build up fast if you aren't honest and open with each other. A good helping of self-awareness and a dash of ego on both sides will serve you well. In the end, you are jointly responsible for your own sexual happiness.

Who's Calling the Shots There's quite a good game a couple can play to find out what each partner is into. It works like this: one night you are in charge, on another your partner is, so that you take it in turns to decide everything that will happen on a particular evening, such as what kind of meal you'll get delivered, which film you'll watch, who will wear what, and so on. Being in charge does not mean testing limits or overstepping boundaries. If there's something that the other person really doesn't want to do, suggest a compromise. The idea of the game is to make it easy to try out new things. And the bonus is that you learn how important it is to express yourself clearly.

You may already have noticed that there is a theme running through this book – the idea of couples talking things over together. So it's time you knew what your reward will be: being able to talk openly about feelings and sex is a real sign of maturity and it also inspires trust. And the pay-off is really good sex.

GIVE IT TO ME!

A lot of what you're experiencing has never happened to you before. You're curious, you're having fun, and it's seriously exciting. Should you be experimenting with new positions? What should you try next?

Talking dirty? Bondage? Anal sex or no anal sex? A threesome? Whatever is on offer, if it's unfamiliar, forget it unless you are sure you like the idea. If you have a bad feeling about it, or you think anyone else will be doing something against their will, don't even

44

think about going there. But if you really fancy it and anybody else who is involved is happy, go for it.

Over time you'll have a lot of different experiences – some great, some not so good. It's a bit like trying out new recipes. You'll be pleasantly surprised by some of the results, but others won't appeal to you at all. Sometimes you need to try a new ingredient a few times before you get used to it, but whether you enjoy it or not will depend on how it's used. It may be, for example, that you find a new position that feels great when you're having sex with one partner and doesn't work at all with another.

There is endless sex on the internet, on television and in magazines. If you've seen scenes in romantic films or porn movies of couples having sex, you've maybe thought: *So that's what it looks like. I suppose that's what I'll have to do.* Wrong. A lot is left out in romantic films, and porn movies have strictly nothing to do with reality. Quite the reverse.

PORN LIES

Penis Length

Male porn actors are selected specifically because they have unusually large penises – at least 20 cm long. Only about one in a hundred men possesses equipment on this scale. The length of an erect European penis ranges from 11 to 17 cm, so the average is 14.27 cm.

It's not the size of the boat, it's the motion of the ocean.
Anonymous

Sperm Fountains

When men climax in porn movies, huge quantities of sperm gush out. All fake! In real life, a guy ejaculates about a teaspoonful.

At It Like Rabbits

In out, in out, in out. The female porn star starts moaning and comes almost immediately. That's a joke. First of all, it takes a whole lot longer than that for a woman to get excited, and secondly, she is not being stimulated properly. It is extremely unlikely that she would come just as a result of a penis pounding in and out of her.

Porn Boobs

A lot of female porn stars have enormous breasts. And astonishingly, they are completely self supporting! But these are gravity-defying fakes. Anyone with largish breasts knows that their weight means they naturally hang down a bit.

Turbo-charged Orgasms

In porn movies, it's common for the women to come almost as soon as they've started having sex – and that is absurd. Also, they have not just one, but multiple orgasms, and always look as though they're having a great time. Lies . . . all lies. Most women need continual stimulation of the clitoris in order to reach a climax.

Swallowing Hard

Women in porn movies adore sucking off their partners, and seem to have no objection at all to semen being sprayed in their faces. This is definitely a matter of taste. Guys, have you ever tasted your semen? Do you enjoy swallowing it? You may agree that there are more delectable mouthfuls.

Below the Belt

Some porn actors have the most intimate parts of their body tattooed – around the anus, for example, or they may have that area chemically lightened (so-called anal bleaching) – in both cases the aim is to make it match the lighter skin surrounding it. Applying chemicals to some of the most sensitive skin on the body, or letting a tattooing pen near it, is certainly risky, and yet this porn fashion is increasingly widely imitated. And almost all porn models wear make-up on their genitals to disguise darker skin, bluish veins or shaving rash.

So now you know: a lot of what you see in porn movies is faked. Even once you've realised this, though, you may still feel that you are expected to do things that you don't find at all erotic. What should you do? First, let's look at why you feel this way. It could well be that you are the source of your own performance anxiety. You think you know what your partner wants, and you 'know' that because you've seen certain things in porn magazines or movies, or you've heard other people talking about them. Usually, though, this isn't the case at all, and there's no need to put yourself under this kind of pressure. Sex between two people is a highly individual and personal experience. It is practically impossible to know beforehand what will please the other person. Each time you have sex with a new partner, you'll discover a different set of likes and dislikes. And the more you find out, the better it gets.

It's very common to fall into the trap of making comparisons, even though this can really get on your partner's nerves: 'Am I better with you than your ex was?', 'Is it as good with me as with your last partner?' Don't. Right from your first sexual encounter, it's likely that your current partner will seem the best so far. The reason is simple: with each partner you have, you become more experienced and more knowledgeable, and, as a result, more sure of yourself and more self-confident. All that know-how, once it has been absorbed, leads to increasing enjoyment. So when, after sex, your partner says, 'That was the best sex I've ever had in my life!', just believe them and luxuriate in how that makes you feel.

Porn and Reality

One to three positions
commonly used in real life

Five to eight positions
often seen in porn films

Sex is infinitely variable, with many thousands of potential subtleties, nuances and variations that you will gradually discover. But it is worth knowing a bit about what men and women tend to like.

Everyone wants to have a partner who enjoys sex. If one of you is aroused, that alone will excite the other. It's great to see your partner feeling turned on. Lots of people react to visual stimuli and prefer to leave the light on during sex, so that they can see as much as possible. Others who are less sure of how they look, or who feel insecure about being naked, would be quite happy if there were a power cut, and are much happier with dim lighting. And as far as porn-style boobs are concerned – it is as untrue that all men like big breasts as it is that all women like big dicks. Outward appearances are a lot less important than people imagine. If you're always thinking about your wobbly thighs or the spot on your backside, you'll be distracted from the important stuff. Focus on touching, closeness, the warmth of the other person's body, and then, as this is about having sex, concentrate on getting as physically close to your partner as possible. Good sex has nothing to do with physical perfection.

WHO AM I?

Sometimes sex can get competitive. Suddenly you're defining yourself not just by your appearance and the people you hang out with, but also by whether you're having sex yet, who you're sleeping with, and how things are going with your partner. Before you know it, you've acquired a sexual reputation.

Girls are sometimes judged not just by how they look and how popular they are, but also by how willing they are to have sex. Put bluntly, that means that boys will suddenly rate even less well-liked girls more highly if they are sexually open-minded. But it works the other way around too: a popular girl who sleeps with lots of boys may find that she's no longer considered such a good friend. If she's really unlucky, she'll be written off as a tramp or a slut. It's easier for boys. They can have sex with lots of girls without damaging their reputations – in fact the reverse is often true.

This is obviously completely unfair. On the other hand, even the coolest guys can get an unwelcome name for themselves pretty fast if it gets around that they are no good in bed. A lot of boys exaggerate or even make things up when they talk about their sexual experiences for fear of what their friends might think of them if they knew the truth. But it is truly stupid to judge anyone according to how much or how little sex they have had. Sex is first and foremost about doing something that's fun and makes you feel good – and this, of course, goes for your partner as well. It shouldn't be about sexual point-scoring and climbing up the popularity ratings. At some time in the future, none of this will seem so important. But right now, your reputation matters enormously to you, and you need somehow to manage it.

The best place to start is to work out for yourself how you feel about sex. Do you tend to be quite extrovert or are you a bit shy? Do you find the idea of sex appealing or are you actually not very interested in it? Do you prefer the opposite sex or your own? Or both? There's a lot to think about, but you can have a great deal of fun finding out the answers. You could try playing different roles: *Shall I be domineering, or quiet and reserved? Am I going to lead or follow? Shall I be wildly outgoing or play hard to get? How are other people reacting to me? What makes me feel good and what doesn't?* You can get a kick out of role-playing like this. But after a while, you might decide that it's easiest just to be you.

Everyone probably thinks that I'm a raving nymphomaniac, that I have an insatiable sexual appetite, when the truth is, I'd rather read a book.
Madonna

48

Here's some food for thought for anyone reading this who is thinking how difficult it seems to be to discover your own sexual identity: by the time you have left school, if not sooner, you'll find that none of this matters very much any more. Even if, at some stage, you've found yourself labelled or called names, as soon as you're with another group of people, the memory of that horrible experience will rapidly disappear.

HOW EMBARRASSING!

Sometimes things happen during sex that seem very funny (at least to one of those involved) or may take a bit of getting used to. And there will be times when you just want the ground to swallow you up. Here are the top five potential showstoppers:

Embarrassing Hair Styles
Seeing your partner naked for the first time can be a shock: maybe you're faced with exuberant, untamed bushes or unexpectedly bald genitals. For some, the 'wrong' style of pubic hair can be a real turn-off, but don't just snigger to yourself – talk about it.

Are you an animal?
Screaming, grunting, yowling – when men and women come, they can make the strangest sounds. Don't be alarmed!

Death Mask
The expression on your partner's face when he or she comes can be appalling – almost like death throes. No surprise, then, that the French refer to orgasm as *la petite mort*, meaning the little death.

Men don't fake orgasm – no man wants to pull a face like that on purpose.
Allan Pease

Special Requests
Toe-sucking? Urinating on your partner (or being urinated on)? Wearing nappies? People can come up with all sorts of unusual requests. Are you up for it? If not, refuse politely.

Gone with the Wind
Sometimes, when a penis enters a vagina, air is pushed in at the same time, and the result is whoopee-cushion-like farting noises. Most common in the doggy position, this can also happen when a man withdraws or when the woman has been lifting and tensing her pelvic floor. The so-called 'vaginal fart' (which is completely odourless) can be dead embarrassing the first time it happens, but once you know what's going on, it's much easier to have a laugh about it.

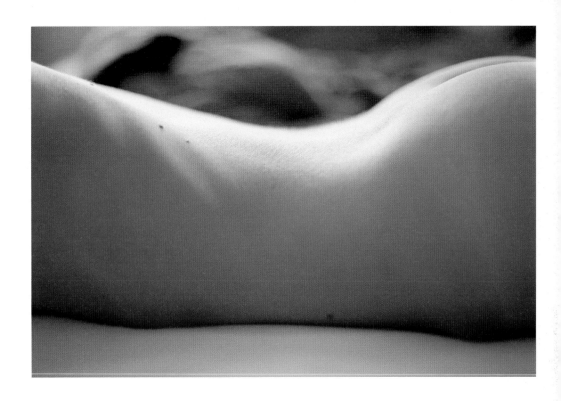

FINDING YOURSELF

SEXUAL IDENTITY

WHO AM I?

The first time just thinking about something makes you excited, or the mere brush of a finger turns you on, your sexual personality – the sexual you – starts to take shape. This side of your personality can develop in a strikingly different way from the rest of you. Maybe you're generally outgoing and rather boisterous, but when you're kissing and cuddling you turn into a pussycat. Or perhaps you're usually a bit shy, but in bed you become wildly extrovert.

It's a good thing to know as much as possible about your own sexuality, and to be aware of how your sexual personality expresses itself. The better you know yourself, the better you'll handle your sexual preferences and desires as well as your fears and insecurities.

Discovering your sexual identity is not just a question of finding out what turns you on, it's also about learning how to handle what you find out. This has nothing to do with whether or not you have partner.

You might want to ask yourself a relevant, but tricky, question. *Who am I?* may be one of the most interesting questions of all time, but it's also very challenging. Some people go on exploring it for the whole of their lives. Coming up with a full answer is about as likely as discovering the meaning of life, but it's still well worth trying.

THE OUTER YOU

You can start finding out who you are by looking at your outward appearance. How you dress and how you behave, for example, reflect both who you are and who you would like to be. Lots of people follow trends created by the fashion industry and the media, but anyone either still at school, or who remembers being there, knows how significant particular details of dress or behaviour can be. One person starts wearing something and pretty soon everyone else in their circle has to have exactly the same footwear or jeans or sunglasses. Anyone wearing this new 'badge' automatically belongs to the group or clique and is identified with whatever it stands for.

At some point, you may get tired of everyone around you looking the same and acting in the same way. It seems boring, and you start wanting a bit of variation, something that expresses your own individuality and differentiates you from everyone else. You're no longer content just to be part of a group. You want to be seen as your own person. And then it's nice to find something that nobody else has. It could be just a detail: shoes that you haven't seen anyone else wearing, an unusual hairstyle, or some music that you've discovered for yourself. When you start to feel like this, it's a sure sign that

KATE LYNN Those are last year's shoes! Kill her!
CAITLIN Also, it's Lisa.
KATE LYNN Kill her twice!
The Simpsons

83

something in you has shifted. Now you're far clearer about how you want others to see you, and you're probably ready to risk looking inwards.

THE INNER YOU

Investigating your inner self comes more easily if you ask yourself a few questions: *What do I think of myself? What do I like and dislike about myself?*

During puberty, a huge amount is changing in you – and fast. Until recently, for example, you were really close to your parents and now it may sometimes feel hard to talk them. How come? You've changed. Your needs and demands are different. The more you go over it in your head, the clearer you become about how and why things are going wrong. If you can possibly put into words what you want, you may well discover that you and your parents can find new ways of relating to one another that are more suited to who you are now.

Why is it so important to find out about yourself? So that you don't let anyone else decide what is right for you. If you've thought carefully and honestly about who you are, you will be more self-assured and self-confident. You'll find it easy to work out what you need, because you'll be used to checking back with yourself, and you'll also be much less likely to run the risk of finding yourself doing things that you don't actually want to do. Recognising our own faults and weaknesses and working on them helps all of us to develop and to become more mature. And the same is true of recognising your own strengths and making the most of them.

You might discover that your outer self is out of sync with the inner you. Perhaps you're good-looking and generally popular: everyone thinks you're great. But secretly you are nowhere near as convinced by yourself and maybe can't bring yourself to believe that people really do admire you. *But they have no idea who I really am!* It might help to start making a list, noting down what you like about your inner and outer selves: the private you and the public you. Which of your characteristics are you happy with? And which are you not so keen on? Just having this discussion with yourself will help you to bring out more of the inner, authentic you.

Everyone experiences self-doubt at some time or another, but relax: you don't have to be liked by everyone. And it's fine if you don't like some things about yourself as long as you value your positive traits too. If you can do that, the real you will shine through.

Having this kind of discussion with yourself will also help in a sexual context. What do you enjoy? And what is definitely not for you? What do you want for yourself? Do you actually know? Don't worry – nothing is set in stone. What satisfies you and what you're

Have a good life. Be a good friend. And try to be completely who you are. And figure out what you personally love. And like go after it with everything you've got no matter how much it takes.
Angelina Jolie

Now I know the things I know, and I do the things I do; and if you do not like me so, to hell, my love, with you.
Dorothy Parker

84

Tattoos

People who regret their tattoos

men
48%

women
25%

Regret according to age when tattoo acquired

before 16 years old
55%

16–20 years old
36%

20–40 years old
26%

Regret according to which part of the body is tattooed

head and neck
11%

arm
39%

abdomen
7%

hand and wrist
10%

back
11%

legs
15%

ankles and feet
7%

comfortable with now may well change later. You might have behaved shyly at first, but now you're happy to be openly sexy. Or you might have tried all sorts of wild stuff to start with and then, later, discover that what you enjoy most is tender, snuggly sex. You may also change your mind about which sexual role you feel happy with: *Do I want to be passive or active? Do I prefer giving a blowjob or receiving one or neither of the above? Do I want to dominate or be dominated? Or am I happy alternating between the two roles?*

Another important aspect of sexual identity has to do with knowing and valuing what you want and having the confidence to express it. Ask yourself very directly *What am I doing for myself? and What am I prepared to do for other people?*

Say there's a girl who likes to have quite energetic sex, while her boyfriend would prefer to take things more gently. That could be a potential source of trouble. But if they talk about their differences, they may find that they're actually not so incompatible after all. Alternatively, they might come to the conclusion that the sex between them just isn't working and never will. A ground rule for all aspects of relationships, including sex, is that nobody should allow themselves to do anything that makes them feel unhappy or uncomfortable. If you do, unhelpful feelings will start to worm their way in, and things will go sour pretty quickly. You might even be put off sex altogether, because it will become associated for you with unpleasant feelings. So it's definitely healthier to sort things out straightaway by talking them through.

THE OTHER ME

Brain, body, hormones – everything is going crazy. And as if all of that wasn't enough to cope with, you've started having really confusing sexual fantasies. A boy might suddenly feel great tenderness towards his (male) friends and even want to express this by hugging or caressing them. Or a girl might have a real urge to give her best girlfriend a proper kiss. *Is this just a passing phase or does this mean that I am gay?*

> **Being Gay** Homosexuality means same-sex sexuality. If two people of the same gender desire each other sexually, and are attracted only to their own sex, they are homosexual (gay or lesbian). A bisexual person is attracted to both sexes.

Some gay men and women know from a very early age that they

are attracted to members of the same sex, and by puberty they're quite clear about their orientation. Other people try out all sorts of things before deciding that they prefer members of their own sex or continue to be attracted to both sexes. Whatever the case, lots of young people have their first sexual experience with someone of their own gender. Often it's far easier than trying to get close to someone of the opposite, still unfamiliar sex. Girls tend to be around girls when they're teenagers, and boys with boys: in the changing rooms before sport, in the shower at the swimming pool, just hanging out chatting. Most boys do what boys have always done, comparing penis lengths, and competing over how far they can pee. Girls eye up each other's breasts. Sometimes the doctors and nurses games kids played when they were very young are revisited, this time with sexual variations.

. . . honestly, I like everything, boyish girls, girlish boys, the heavy and the skinny.
Angelina Jolie

> **Changing Times . . . Changing Attitudes** In 1989 Denmark became the first country in the world to allow gay couples to enter into registered partnerships, and in 2001 the Netherlands became the first country to legalise same-sex marriage. By August 2013, fifteen countries (Argentina, Belgium, Brazil, Canada, Denmark, France, Iceland, the Netherlands, New Zealand, Norway, Portugal, Spain, South Africa, Sweden, Uruguay) and several states in Mexico and the United States had legislated to allow same-sex couples to marry. Same-sex marriage laws came into effect in England and Wales in 2014, and Scotland may soon follow this lead, while Northern Ireland has rejected the idea. Elsewhere the possibility has either not been raised or legalisation attempts have been defeated, but polls in various countries show that public support for same-sex marriage continues to rise.

I don't have to make the choice, I like girls and I like boys.
Peaches, I U She

How do you sort out these confusing, chaotic feelings? Say you are a girl attracted to a girlfriend. How long does this feeling last for? A few days? Or is it more like months? Do you long to be physically intimate with her, or do you just think she's a really lovely person? Do you feel attracted to other girls?

Around puberty, people often have feelings of intense affection for their friends. Sometimes when boys get together, they'll talk about loving each other, but that doesn't necessarily mean they want to have sex together. Having said that, a lot of girls and boys do experiment with partners of their own sex, for example, boys play boisterous games in the showers after sport, and girls become very close – sitting on each other's laps, stroking each other's hair, and so on. This sort of behaviour doesn't mean that those taking part are homosexual. If you are clear that you are only ever attracted to members of your own sex, though, you probably are gay or bisexual.

Heterosexuality is not normal, it's just common.
Dorothy Parker

87

Animal Romance There are countless examples of homosexuality in the animal world. Same-sex relationships have so far been observed in more than 1000 different animal species, from dolphins to gorillas. In Hawaii, scientists studying Laysan albatrosses noticed that 31% of the albatross pairs were lesbian. Pairs of male penguins observed in zoos have been known to steal an egg so as to hatch it themselves and bring up the chick. And it's estimated that around 10% of domesticated rams are homosexual.

It takes some people quite a long time to figure out where they belong sexually, and others who have a good idea of their orientation are afraid to come out. A man can live for years – even decades – with a woman and even have children with her, before finally recognising that he actually wants to be with another man. The same thing can happen to women. Important and profound feelings will have been repressed for a long time. With a few notable exceptions, top sports people have often chosen not to come out for fear of losing fans and sponsorship. But increasing numbers of people in public positions are open about their sexuality, although this is far easier in the more liberal parts of Europe and North America, Australia and New Zealand than elsewhere. Here, society has become more accepting of homosexuality, although some prejudice against gays still lingers on. Young gay people, whether male or female, still have to come to terms with feeling 'different'.

Gay slang Like all slang, gay slang changes with the times. Some expressions are incomprehensible outside the LGBT (Lesbian Gay Bisexual Transgender) community, others pass into more general usage. If you are straight, you probably haven't heard 'vegetarian', used to refer to a gay man who doesn't do oral sex, or 'chicken', meaning a young gay male seeking older men. But you might know that 'butch', for example, is used to describe the more masculine, dominating partner in a lesbian couple, while 'femme' is the more feminine one. Coded language and signs are sometimes used by members of the LGBT scene to make themselves known to each other (so-called 'gaydar'), but they are also useful where homosexuality is illegal, or where there is hostility towards gays in the wider community.

As far as I was concerned, men were something you had around the place, not particularly interesting, but quite harmless. I had never shown the slightest feeling for them, and apart from my never wearing a skirt, saw nothing else in common between us.
Jeanette Winterson, Oranges Are Not the Only Fruit

Many parents feel they neither understand homosexuality nor know much about it, so they avoid the subject altogether. This can make it hard for young gay people to come to terms with their own sexuality. They may even find that some of their straight friends feel challenged.

Sometimes the best thing to do is to contact one of the organisations set up especially to give support to gay people whether by answering questions and giving advice, or simply by providing a sympathetic, knowledgeable person to talk to when you are preparing to come out or want to explain how you feel to your parents. There are gay clubs and organisations where young people can meet up, as well as forums on the internet. Contact details for some of these can be found on page 250.

COMFORTABLE IN YOUR SKIN?

A few people have all the physical attributes of one gender but feel emphatically that they belong to the other one. Many of them are aware of this disconnect from an early age, sometimes from childhood. *I am physically a woman, but I feel like a man, and I wanted to be regarded as a man* – or the other way around. If your external physical appearance does not match your inner self, you are a transsexual. It is more common for men than women to be transsexual. (Some people prefer the term transgender, others just use trans.)

The feeling of being trapped in the wrong body can be so clear and unequivocal that a person will often go to great lengths to make his or her body and appearance resemble that of the opposite sex, even to the extent of having gender reassignment surgery. But seeing this through is neither easy nor straightforward.

You need considerable inner strength and staying power to cope with undergoing such a radical physical transformation. It isn't just a matter of thinking one day that you might prefer to be a woman rather than a man (or vice versa). Those who yearn for a complete physical transition will have had a profound sense, for as long as they can remember, of having the wrong sexual characteristics: *I am a woman, I just happen to have a penis,* or *I am a man, but my body has a vagina.* Anyone contemplating transition has to be prepared to undertake years of investigations in hospital, and to submit to seemingly endless questioning about lifestyle, personal history and sexuality by the authorities and the medical profession. And all this with no guarantee that permission to have the relevant operations will be granted. But for those who truly want and need to achieve this hard-to-win goal, transition can be a liberation.

If you really love cross-dressing – putting on clothes usually worn by the opposite sex – but have no desire to make fundamental changes to your body, you are a transvestite (or cross-dresser). The general public often thinks of transvestites as scandalous, exotic creatures, probably from seeing coverage of the famous carnival in Rio, or because of the way they are portrayed on television and in movies, but most people who cross-dress – and for that matter most transsexuals – are far from exhibitionist. They are more likely to repress or hide their true inclinations – unsurprisingly, given that they have to endure so much insensitivity and intolerance.

More (mainly heterosexual) men than women are transvestites. The proportion of male transvestites who are gay is exactly the same as for the general male population.

People often confuse transvestism and transsexuality, but they have nothing to do with each other. A transsexual has a gender identity that does not match the body he or she inhabits. A transvestite or cross-dresser simply has a fetish for wearing the clothes of the opposite sex: *I am a man and I sometimes like dressing as a woman, but that doesn't mean I want to be one.*

Many people regard transvestites and transsexuals as suffering from an illness. This sort of attitude can have severe psychological consequences, particularly for transsexuals. There are organisations that offer help and advice to both groups (see page 250).

The Third Gender? In some cultures, homosexuals, transsexuals and transvestites have traditionally been given certain functions and responsibilities. So-called 'two-spirits' (two spirits in one body) existed in over 130 Native American tribes across North America. A biologically male two-spirit would dress as a woman, and take on a woman's role in the community, while a female two-spirit often wore men's clothes, did men's work and was allowed to take wives. Often, two-spirits alternated between the sexes in the clothes they wore and the work they did, never entirely committing to either.

The Vedic scripts (sacred Hindu texts) refer to a third sex which includes homosexuals, transsexuals, transvestites and eunuchs (castrated men). These individuals were thought to possess special spiritual powers, a belief that persists in some traditional communities in India even today.

In Europe and North America, and indeed wherever Western dress became the norm, there was a time when all women wore dresses and all men wore trousers. The idea of a woman wearing trousers was unthinkable, and around 1900, when a few women began to do so, it was regarded as scandalous, indecent behaviour.

Of course the reasons for wearing trousers are obvious: they allow far more freedom of movement than skirts do, it's fine to stand or sit with your legs apart, and they're warmer. Trouser-wearing women are no longer judged to be in some way abnormal or sexually dysfunctional because attitudes and opinions in the general population have changed fundamentally over the last 100 years. It works the other way around too: male models sometimes appear on the catwalk wearing designer skirts, and some Scots wear kilts, but nobody presumes that this makes them all transvestites.

DEFINING BOUNDARIES

Whether you are gay, straight, bisexual or trans, there are some important questions you need to ask yourself about boundaries and personal space. *Where do my boundaries lie? And how about the other person?* You may well find that you like to keep most people at a distance – far enough away that they couldn't possibly touch you. It can even feel uncomfortable to be in the same room as someone else. Here's a brief exercise that will help you to understand more about your own personal space – and that of other people.

COME A BIT CLOSER

You and your partner should stand about six to eight metres apart, and then both start moving towards each other. Each of you has to indicate with your hand when you feel that the other person has entered your personal space, then make another sign when you feel that your partner has come close enough. You might find yourselves making both signs at almost the same time or, alternatively, you might feel that the other person already feels too close when they're still some distance away. It can be interesting to try this exercise with people you don't know particularly well, or, on the other hand, with your parents, or your little brother, say. And it's certainly a good idea to try it out with your partner.

How we perceive other people in general has a lot to do with how we will relate to a partner. And we react in different ways to strangers depending on whether we meet them out in the street or inside. Outside you may have to raise your voice because you're competing with all sorts of background noise, whereas in a theatre, say, you tend to speak in a much lower voice. If you're out in the open air with someone, it's simple enough to take a step backwards, but you can't do that on a crowded bus. Being so close to a person that you can actually smell them is usually pretty unpleasant. On the other hand, if you're crammed into a kitchen with a crowd of friends at a party, you might feel fine about being pressed up against someone you quite like.

Too Close for Comfort People tend to keep a natural distance between themselves and others, especially if they don't know one another. In our culture, we usually keep far enough away from another person that we can see their whole body. If you get closer, so that only the top half of their body is in sight, you will have entered that individual's personal space. By now you are near enough to touch. Anything closer than 20 cm away counts as pretty intimate. At that distance, you will be able to smell perfume or sweat on the other person. Think about the distance you like there to be between you and other people: teachers, parents, friends, for example.

It's important to know how close you are prepared to let someone get to you, and at exactly which point their closeness becomes oppressive. A lot of people have rather limited awareness of this, or daren't express how they feel about it. If you get into the habit of noticing how other people are feeling, as well as paying attention to the space you need yourself, it will become much easier to take avoiding action or tell people when they're crowding you, or to communicate that they can come closer. Feeling confident enough to be clear about these things will automatically raise your self-esteem. And you'll find it easier to work out what you actually want. This is just a start, but how you instinctively feel about your personal space and the way you act as a result play an important part in how well you deal with closeness and trust, or with invitations and rejections.

Of course you may find yourself dealing with someone who does not recognise personal boundaries – whether at a party, at work or during sex. Knowing about body language can come in very useful. You'll probably be sending out signals anyway, without realising it. So it's good use to know how to use it deliberately when you need it, and to be able to decode other people's signals.

Your behaviour communicates a lot: if you like someone, you automatically turn towards them. Your body will be open, and you'll tend to lean slightly towards them and try to make eye contact. On the other hand, if you want to keep your distance from someone, you will probably turn away, maybe folding your arms in front of you, and if the other person comes too close, you may take a step backwards.

One thing is certain: a person who seems stressed or uptight is almost always a turn-off. You can tell that someone is tense if their breathing is shallow, they don't know what to do with their hands, they stand stiffly in front of you or they shift nervously from foot to foot. These signs usually indicate fear, insecurity, someone who is ill at ease, or even aggression and anger. On the other hand, too little energy or tension sends a couldn't-care-less, bored signal, even if this is not how the person really feels. Body language that communicates this message includes slumped shoulders, a rounded back and a limp, unenthusiastic manner. Nobody is likely to be attracted by that kind of presentation. But if you're lively and come across as friendly and interested, you can have completely the opposite effect.

OVERSTEPPING THE MARK

It's helpful to discover where your personal space begins and ends and to be able to defend it. This will enable you to decide what is likely to do you good and what might harm you. If you can master this, you'll find it easier to weigh up what's right for you and what's wrong. One of the trickiest situations to cope with is when you like someone, you're both flirting, you're quite happy with what is going on, but then your partner suddenly wants to go further and you're not at all sure you want to or whether you can refuse.

He was really sweet with me at the party. When he came round to my house later, my parents weren't in. We were on the sofa and started kissing and he wanted to go further, but I said I didn't want to. He said he wanted to find out just how sexy I was. I said again that I didn't want to. But he ignored me, pulled my underwear down and pushed into me. I just wanted it to be over as fast as possible. I cried. He said I shouldn't get upset, we had both wanted it. I feel ashamed, and that it's my fault that it happened, because I was attracted to him in the first place.

. . . It's not always a simple yes/no, e.g. you may have done other sexual acts, but you still have a right to say no. I definitely didn't undersatnd that at 15 and my first sexual encounters definitely involved blurred consent.
Anonymous female respondent to a Sex Education Forum survey

You always have a right to stop what is going on if it feels wrong for you, and that applies whether you are with someone you like and know well or someone you've just met.

If you are open with yourself about what feels comfortable and right, you will instinctively know what is an acceptable level of physical contact between you and someone else. Does being touched by an uncle or aunt feel appropriate and loving, or does it go too far? Is it OK if an instructor at a sports training session grasps your hip to show you how to do something, or is it unnecessary and invasive? Are you happy if your mother kisses you on the mouth? Even if you are not yet familiar with exactly where your own boundaries lie, remember that adults almost always know very well where they are. Unfortunately, though, some of them will still cross the line.

My mother really wants me to go to sleep in her bed, because she finds it comforting. Sometimes she asks me what type of underwear I prefer her in. I think she should decide that.

Every morning I have to put up with him having a pee in front of me. He may be my father, but I still don't want him to see me naked, and I don't want him looking at my body. I keep telling him that I want to be on my own in the bathroom, but he says I shouldn't make such a fuss.

Boundaries can be overstepped psychologically as well as physically. If a request like 'I want to be on my own in the bathroom' is ignored, that is crossing a boundary. It can be quite hard to know exactly where the boundaries lie between adults and children, especially as feelings and behaviour change so radically during puberty. Something that was absolutely fine when a child was younger will suddenly feel completely unacceptable. Being together in the bathroom might have been no problem before, but now it is unbearable.

If you say 'no' and you're ignored, and you end up doing something against your will because you have been caught out, trapped, forced or threatened, that is abuse. And that applies not just to sex. Invasive touching or insinuating remarks are also forms of bullying and domination. Nobody should have to put up with that kind of behaviour.

Perpetrators almost always try to intimidate their victims, manipulating them and persuading them that what they're doing (or 'what we're doing' as they'll often put it) is 'perfectly normal' and/or 'our little secret'. But the better you get to know yourself, the more certain you will be that this kind of situation is definitely not OK. And when that happens, it can be easiest to deal with it by getting some help. Talk to an adult or contact one of the organisations listed on pages 250-251. Listen to your inner voice. If you feel uncomfortable or ill at ease, remember that everyone has the right, at any moment, to say 'no' or 'stop', regardless of how the other person feels about that. This can be pretty difficult if you're dealing with a parent, your grandfather or the nice lady next door, but the fact is that abuse usually involves people who are well-known to the victim. There is strong statistical evidence that most sexual abuse is carried out by close friends and family members. Sadly, someone who has been abused as a child or young person will often choose a partner who habitually oversteps other people's sexual boundaries, or may act in that way themselves.

When someone's sexual privacy has been invaded, that person often feels ashamed and somehow responsible for what has happened. Even if you feel this way, it is still really important to speak to an adult about it. If you have been raped, you will need to have a medical examination (whether you are male or female) to check that you have not picked up an infection or been hurt. And if you are a teenage girl, you may, of course, have become pregnant. The doctor you see will be able to refer you to a psychologist if you need further help. And although this is really hard to do, it's important to report what has happened to the police. It might just prevent the person responsible for hurting you from doing the same thing to others.

Sexting usually means send and receiving 'nudes' (naked pictures), 'underwear shots', sexual or 'dirty pics', rude text messages or videos via a mobile phone or tablet. You might sext because you're proud of your body and it makes you feel sexy, or as a joke. It often happens because people think that 'everyone is doing it', or someone is worried that they might be seen as 'frigid' or 'shy' if they don't. Or maybe someone pressures you for pictures, or you feel you 'owe' it to a boy or girlfriend. Whatever the reason, be aware that once you've pressed 'send', a photo or video is no longer in your control. It's been estimated (by the Internet Watch Foundation) that 88% of self-made explicit images are 'stolen' from their original upload location (typically, social networks) and made available on other websites, in particular, porn sites. See pages 250-251 for details of websites with more information about sexting and advice about what to do if you're upset by it.

SEDUCTION

Seducing someone is not easy. That's why there are so many books on the art of seduction. What it comes down to is convincing another person that they like you and that they want to do what you want to do. You might have met or spotted someone you really fancy, and you're keen to hook up with them. Or maybe it's a day when you can't wait to go to bed with your partner, or perhaps you would just like to enjoy a cosy night in together. The crucial first stage if you want to seduce someone is getting to know them.

Nowadays, it is increasingly unusual in developed countries for a girl to wait for a boy to make the first move. Girls can, and do, take the first step. The important thing is to have received a positive signal from the person you're interested in before you make your approach. It's best not to move in on someone before you know you are in with a chance. Usually, people start by swapping interested glances. There'll be a clear signal in that exchange, and one of the two will make the first move. At this point, both of you need to be as brave and as unambiguous as possible. Many people tend, out of insecurity, to send out a lukewarm amber signal, while thinking that they are communicating an enthusiastic green. How sure you are of yourself, and how confident, depends on positive self esteem. Someone who is used to being noticed and respected will usually appear relatively relaxed, self-confident and at ease with themselves, whereas a person who has mainly experienced rejection will be less self-confident. But even if it's not always easy for you, don't give up!

Any idiot can get laid when they're famous. It's getting laid when you're not famous that takes some talent.
Kevin Bacon

Exactly why and how does flirting work? A lot of scientific studies have tried to find out. Obviously it has to do with appearance and the effect that one person has on another. On a first meeting, pheromones play a big part. Pheromones are biochemical signals, unique to each individual, that are subconsciously picked up on by others. It takes just a few milliseconds for your body to decide whether or not someone is a potential new partner. As soon as a woman is close enough to smell someone, a decision over the other person's pheromones is as good as taken. Then it's a question of how similar the two individuals' immune systems are. The more different they are, the more positive the woman's reaction. Why? Because two different immune systems are more likely than two similar ones to produce robust, healthy children. So it seems that it is when their pheromones are a good match that a woman finds a man attractive and gives him the 'go' signal. And how about men? Unfortunately, they appear to have no influence over this unconscious decision process. It's interesting, though, that the contraceptive pill changes how a woman responds to pheromones. Women using this form of contraception would do well to back up their choice of men with other information.

BUTTERFLY HUNTERS

Here's a game that will help you to find out a bit about your own dating characteristics. First you select which dating type you most resemble out of four basic types:

There is the Hunter who makes straight for his or her prey, but who targets only one person at a time. Then there is the Casanova type, who also makes the first move, but, unlike the Hunter, is likely to have more than one iron in the fire.

The Romantic plays a passive game, waiting until he is approached. He dreams of having a single, wonderful, perfect partner. The Butterfly is also passive, but, while being happy to flirt with anyone and everyone, is unlikely to settle with one person.

All of these types are found in both sexes. Which of these do you resemble the most? Of course, it's sometimes hard to decide exactly which profile you fit. But take a look at our diagram opposite. The Romantic type is at bottom left, but exactly where he or she belongs depends on the axes, as we'll now explain:

The vertical axis indicates how proactive someone is – whether he or she usually makes the first move (active) or not (passive). The horizontal axis indicates whether you usually gravitate towards one person at a time or tend to have several partners on the go simultaneously. Someone with a lot of contacts would be on the right, and a person with only one partner on the left.

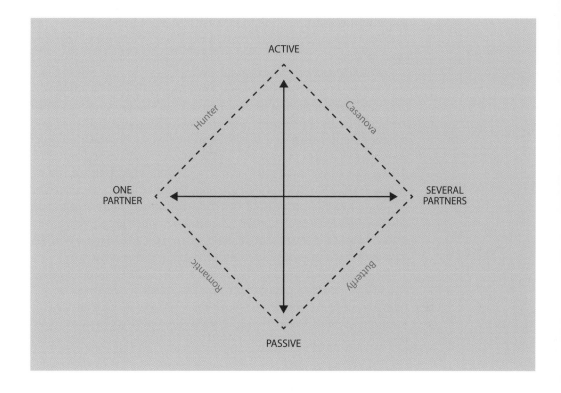

Say you're a Romantic type, so you tend to be passive, but, when the mood takes you, you feel fine about hooking up with several people, then your position in the lower left part of the diagram will move up a bit. If it's not unusual for you to be involved with two people simultaneously, then you're verging towards the Butterfly type.

AND IN A RELATIONSHIP?

It may be that when you are dating, you are an active type, but once you are in a relationship, you tend to be passive. Equally, you might continue to be active, always making the first approach, having the ideas and leading. Someone who just wants as many experiences as possible and who doesn't want to commit to one person is a Casanova.

It might be that, over the course of your life, you will take on the role of different types at various times. Lots of people reach a point when they want children and a family, and that can completely change the type(s) of partner they go for and how they behave towards them. Anyone who broadcasts how many partners he or she has at the same time (Casanova) or never stops flirting (Butterfly) is going to find it hard to find someone willing to get serious with them, because these kinds of behaviour have 'lack of commitment' written all over them.

The interesting thing, though, is that a person's fundamental energy and whether or not they tend to behave actively or passively usually stay the same.

So which types do best together?

There's no easy answer to that question: different combinations produce different outcomes. If you go after a Hunter, then you'll obviously be with someone who likes the thrill of the pursuit. In that kind of relationship, you need to know that after the first flush of interest in each other, you'll go on enjoying being 'hunted' and making the effort to keep the attention of your partner – by alternating between being cold and affectionate, for example. On the other hand if two passive types get together, they'll need to take care that their relationship doesn't stall through inactivity, because they are both people who prefer not to take the initiative. So, the dynamic in a relationship has a lot to do with the type of person you get together with.

The diagram on the previous page is not perfect, but it may help you to start thinking about who you are, how you handle yourself, how you are perceived, which types you tend to seek out. You may, for example, be most drawn to people of the same dating type as yourself.

EVERYDAY SEDUCTION

Maybe you've already found someone who's perfect for you. If so, you'll probably already have some experience of seduction. When you've just fallen in love you have it easy – hormones take care of pretty much everything. All it takes is a glance or a gesture and you're all over each other. That's the initial passionate phase, but it may not be quite so simple when things start to get a bit routine. This is when you need to think about how to go on attracting, or seducing, your partner. It can make a big difference to the quality of a relationship if you keep making an effort by continuing to show an interest in the other person, being attentive, remaining open, taking care of both yourself and your partner, and making an effort with your appearance. And that goes for both sexes.

Love is about seduction, not about possessing the heart of another.
Marlene Dietrich

> **Absolute Beginners** Everyone longs to be seduced. The feeling that someone else is interested in you, desires you, wants to have sex with you is, for most people, irresistible. Ideally, partners should take it in turns to make the first move.

In Hollywood movies, seductive women tend to wear suspenders and red lipstick, whether they want to go to bed with a man or (as in James Bond movies) they are trying to extract information or some kind of favour from him. In real life, though, seduction doesn't always involve sexy underwear. It has more to do with working out how to win someone over while at the same time satisfying your own needs. And that is as true for men as it is for women. Everyone can seduce or be seduced.

Seduction isn't always just about sex. You might, for example, want to get someone to go to a movie with you, or come out with you to see some friends one evening. But if your main aim is to excite someone's sexual interest, here are a few strategies you can try. Remember, though, that everyone reacts differently, so your best guide is your partner's body language. That will tell you whether your advances are hitting the spot or not.

LIP SERVICE

She wraps her arms around him and kisses his neck. He tightens his grasp on her buttocks, presses his pelvis gently against hers and whispers in her ear. Another great beginning is for him to take her face in his hands and smother it with little kisses. She may well lean further into him if she wants more. Later, if he feels like it, he could, gently but firmly, hold her hands behind her back and then softly press himself against her. She will then feel some of the weight of his body, and maybe begin to imagine what it would feel like to go further.

What you're trying to do is to show that you're thinking of taking things further than just cuddling, and that you're feeling really sexy. It's important to make the prospect of getting intimate with each other so appealing that your partner simply can't resist it. What you do not want is someone coming along for the ride just to please you.

That's true whether you're dealing with sex or not. If you want someone to go to a concert with you, for example, showing how enthusiastic you are about the idea is a good start, and then you could get them really interested by mentioning something that you know will appeal, like the name of a particular musician or the venue you have in mind. If it works, you might find that the next time it's your friend who is suggesting a night out. The best seducers are flexible and creative and that gives them a good chance of getting together with the person they are trying to attract.

Conversation plays a key role in sexual seduction. Almost everyone likes to be paid compliments and told how sexy they are. And there are many, many ways of telling your friend how much you fancy them. Make sure you express yourself clearly. And don't forget that you can win someone over just with your eyes: a seductive, suggestive look can be far more powerful than words.

When you fish for love, bait with your heart, not with your brain.
Mark Twain

> **One Size Fits All?** Every individual has his or her own strategies for seduction, especially when it comes to sex. And everyone reacts differently to come-ons. One person might find red lace underwear irresistible, while to another it just seems cheap. Some people find certain accessories really important, others can take them or leave them. Some people want to get down to having sex straight away, others prefer to lead up to it more gradually.

NOT RIGHT NOW . . .

Who dares doesn't necessarily win. And that can hurt. So how should you react when your advances towards your friend or partner are rejected?

First: don't be offended! It's hard not to be, of course. It's also not easy to keep smiling if it's obvious what you would like to happen and you don't get the reaction you expected. But taking offence or sulking won't get you anywhere. You haven't necessarily done anything wrong. Don't forget that there are times when you don't feel like having sex either. As long as this isn't a permanent development, it's not the end of the world.

It's not a good idea to act disappointed, hurt or anxious when your advances are rejected. That can be a real turn-off for your partner, who may well also feel annoyed that you don't seem to care at all about what she or he needs. If this does happen, you'll both be caught in a negative spiral. Suddenly a whole week has gone by with no sex, or two weeks . . . or even longer. Both partners begin to get entrenched in their own positions.

And then the big guns start to be wheeled out. You could almost say that it's seduction in reverse. Here are a few examples of what people can resort to over a few days or weeks after they have experienced rejection:

- cold-shouldering, not talking, drawing back, acting offended, withdrawing affection
- being demanding, trying to correct the other person, analysing everything they say or demanding explanations
- belittling, pressuring, showing impatience, bickering, blaming
- holding grudges and rejecting sexual advances, being provocative or bitchy
- making the other person feel bad
- point-scoring, being pushy or overbearing
- begging, being clingy or using emotional blackmail

With challenging behaviour like this, any erotic charge in the

Once a woman has forgiven her man, she must not reheat his sins for breakfast.
Marlene Dietrich

relationship will simply disappear. You'll be incapable of seeing anything but the negative aspects of your partner. And the more you dwell on these, the angrier and more dissatisfied you will become.

How do you think you are at dealing with this kind of stuff? How do you act when you've been rejected? A good way to react is to continue behaving seductively, but just to tone it down a little. This is all about making yourself as appealing as possible, and that has to do with a lot more than just looks. So, although you're disappointed, try to go on being affectionate and light-hearted. You could maybe smile and say something like, 'Oh! OK – I'll take back that irresistible offer!' That way you'll get your partner on your side. And sex will be back on the menu all the sooner – for both of you. So to keep sexual attraction alive over a long time, it's important to:

- learn to cope with being turned down without reproaching or blaming the other person
- think about how to show your best side to your partner without making things up or pretending
- never forget the importance of seduction (keep in mind that knowing and understanding your own, as well as your partner's needs will make all the difference)

If your advances are invariably rejected, you perhaps need to think about whether there might be something fundamental between you that isn't working.

Mindgames Imagine a situation in which you have been rejected sexually, and think about how you would react: would you be irritated? bitter? offended? sad? Then imagine a completely different set of reactions: smile, try to be as laid back as possible and make light of what has happened. Say how you're feeling, but make sure that your partner realises that you're not hurt or offended, and that you aren't taking this rejection the wrong way. There's always another time.

CONFLICTS

Having a close girlfriend or boyfriend, being in a relationship, can be wonderful. You find yourself spending huge amounts of time with the person you love, sharing experiences, thoughts and feelings and having fun (and sex) together. Of course life as a couple is not always easy. Sometimes relationships can become quite tricky, and

I love you. You annoy me more than I ever thought possible but . . . I want to spend every irritating moment with you.
Scrubs

the other person may begin to annoy you quite a lot. But don't give up too soon.

The younger you are, the less likely you are to put up with your partner's little idiosyncrasies, and the more likely it is that you'll go looking for new experiences instead. At some point, though, you may want something that lasts for more than a few weeks or months. This is where two magic qualities come in: patience and tolerance. You'll need to be patient with your partner, who will almost certainly not entirely understand you straight away, and you'll have to tolerate things being done differently from the way you do them. Also, you probably won't share all the same values and opinions. In a partnership, you cannot expect everything to go exactly as you'd like it to. It's much more a case of finding a middle way that you can both agree on.

Here are a couple of examples of basic problems that commonly come up in relationships, and suggestions of ways you might deal with them.

Let's start with disappointment. *He's late again. She's off sex again.* Most people tend to blame the other person for their disappointment, because he or she hasn't done what they were expected to do. And that's the heart of the problem – our desires are not the same as those of our partners. If you're always feeling disappointed by the other person, maybe it's time to think about adjusting your expectations. For example, someone who consistently arrives late may seriously annoy you, but maybe, if he is always fifteen minutes behind schedule, you could get into the habit of allowing for this. Then you could avoid all those feelings of disappointment and annoyance.

This is about developing a good level of understanding of the other person. For example, after a hard day at work, your girlfriend may not feel any desire to have sex. If she feels that you understand this, it will recreate the intimacy between you, and you might even find that she wakes up the next morning feeling sexy again.

Sometimes you need to think about how clearly you have expressed what you want. Unfortunately, most of us are not mindreaders. So if you're able to explain what you would like and have the confidence to talk about it, you'll definitely notice the difference, because your partner will have a much better idea about what you would like to happen.

A classic problem in relationships is jealousy. It can turn perfectly nice people into fiends: 'Where were you?' 'Who were you with?' 'Why didn't you call me?' And the green-eyed monster usually comes equipped with good amounts of snooping and paranoia. Jealousy wells up when a person feels insecure in a relationship. Maybe you can't believe that your partner really wants to be with you, or perhaps you feel that you don't deserve them? It's hard to get yourself out of thinking like this. The more you try to prove your love for your partner, the more likely it is that he or she will become infuriated and turn away from you. Before you know it, you've dug your own grave – or at least brought the relationship to an end. If you find that it keeps happening to you, that each time you're with someone it's not long before you start feeling jealous, it is worth trying to work on this. Otherwise happiness and contentment are almost bound to elude you.

Sometimes, though, there is a good reason for feeling insecure in a relationship – if your partner really is being unfaithful. If you've been betrayed before, whether it was just once or several times, and you've had to battle through the resulting anguish, you're bound to be more cautious the next time you get together with someone. Explaining these anxieties to your partner can go a long way to creating understanding while you work through your feelings.

There are lots of reasons why people cheat on their partners. Although it is not an excuse, sometimes it is genuinely a one-off: it might have happened after a lot of alcohol has been drunk or when a relationship is already in deep trouble. But there are some people who have attachment issues which lead them to deliberately sabotage a relationship with serial cheating, because they can't cope with getting close to a permanent partner. Others may need a second sexual partner to live out sides of their personality that are repressed in the main relationship. Or it could be low self-esteem that makes someone sleep around repeatedly to bolster how they feel about themselves. Whatever the reason, anyone who finds themselves cheating on their partner on a regular basis needs to think hard about why they are prepared to risk their relationship in this way. And the person who is knowingly being betrayed and yet stays with their partner must ask themselves why they are prepared to go along with this behaviour.

Disappointment, jealousy, being unfaithful: these three problems all have to do with people's sense of self worth. A person who likes him or herself and has self-respect will not tolerate being treated badly for very long, and, conversely, won't treat someone else badly. People who like themselves are able to trust others and to give their partners enough space: characteristics that are fundamental to a long and happy partnership.

But there is another common hazard in all human interactions that can become a serious problem in relationships: misunderstandings. *She says that she doesn't want anything to eat, and then she's offended because I haven't left anything for her. That really annoys me.*

Communication is not always straightforward. Sometimes it's as though you and your partner speak different languages. What the other person says can seem unnecessarily complicated, illogical, ignorant or insensitive. Misunderstanding between men and women happens so often that a car crash is almost inevitable at some point. We'll give you a couple of examples of the issues that come up most often. It goes without saying that men and women are equally likely to act like this. In which of the scenes we are about to describe do you feel closer to the man, and in which to the woman?

Men often say exactly what they want. Unfortunately, women sometimes can't take what they have been told at face value, so they'll ask: 'Are you sure?', 'Wouldn't you prefer to have this one or maybe that one?' Incessant questioning of this kind can be infuriating because as far as the man is concerned, the matter has already been settled.

Why do women do this? Because it's what they would like to happen to them, and they think they're just being thoughtful. They would love it if their partner sometimes checked whether they need anything or could do with some help. That's why a lot of women cannot understand why a man gets so annoyed just because she has asked a couple of times whether he is happy with something.

Men have a similar difficulty: *I've asked her if I can help with anything, and she said no. So why did she get so worked up when I picked up my phone?* It helps to accept a few givens here: there will inevitably be differences between you, and you will both need to bring some understanding of the other person to the situation. Try to meet in the middle. Perhaps she could ask fewer questions, and he could ask more.

And another thing: misunderstandings tend to snowball when problems are being discussed. She wants to broaden things out and examine every last detail from every angle, but for him, the details are unimportant. He will come straight to the point and offer a solution, but she isn't after a solution – she's probably already come up with one herself. She wants to be able to discuss things. If he brings the conversation to an end by offering a solution, the reproaches and accusations will come thick and fast, and he won't have a clue why this is happening to him. What can be done? Women could try to be more brief, and men could try to be more understanding. A sympathetic response is often more important to women than the actual solution.

And now the most challenging discipline of all: criticism. If there's something you want to change, it's important to make your request by referring to yourself. 'I would really like to go for a walk with you', rather than 'You never go for a walk with me'. Reproaches and accusations are pointless because they just make your partner feel attacked. It's better to play a defensive game; that way your partner is more likely to want to join in. You can reinforce your request with positive body language. If you practise pointing things out in this way, you'll seem really friendly. Your request has been raised, and your partner has the chance to catch the ball gracefully and run with

From now on I'll never leave the room without saying how much I love you and . . . this takes a long time. Maybe a pat on the butt will do. . . that's it.
Homer, in The Simpsons

104

it. There's been no conflict, and everyone knows where they stand. Yes, relationships sometimes have to be worked at. But what you get as a result is priceless: at best, a partner who loves you, will stand by you through thick and thin and who can accept you, warts and all – and, of course, who likes going to bed with you.

Selfishness is not living as one wishes to live, it is asking others to live as one wishes to live.
Oscar Wilde

> **NB!** Think about what your partner would really like rather than just giving them what you enjoy.

HOOKING UP

There's no doubt that you can have a lot of fun as a single. But you can also find yourself on your own when that was not your intention at all. Perhaps you have not yet hooked up with anyone, or it might be a long time since you last had a partner. Maybe the relationships you've been in tend to end suddenly before they've had a chance to get off the ground. And you yearn to be with someone. Sometimes this longing can be so strong that it actually hurts. Then you may feel desperate and start to brood on your situation. *Is there something wrong with me? Why can't I get it right?* But that kind of question will lead you in completely the wrong direction. It's far more useful to ask *Who am I?* and *What am I looking for?*

You need to be fairly precise about this. Other people will appreciate the real you only if you yourself have a good idea about who you are, and you are able to express yourself clearly and honestly. Then people will start getting interested. The same applies to your search for a partner. The better idea you have of what qualities you're looking for in someone, the easier it will be. It's like using a search engine. The more accurate your keywords are, the better the hit rate. If you've had no luck so far, you need to do a more careful search, or at least be clearer about what you're after. So how do you work that out?

First, let's look at you. We've already discussed this a bit. Ideally, you've already thought about who you are and what your particular qualities are. But we can now narrow things down even further by using our Circles of Love diagram over the page.

You can either draw the Circles of Love for yourself or copy the diagram, and then fill it in once for yourself, and once for your partner. (You might want to think about where your ex would fit in the diagram. It could explain why things didn't work out.) You start by entering your own characteristics, and noting how pronounced they are. It can take a while to be satisfied with what you've written. What's the point of doing this? Well, if, for example, you have a good

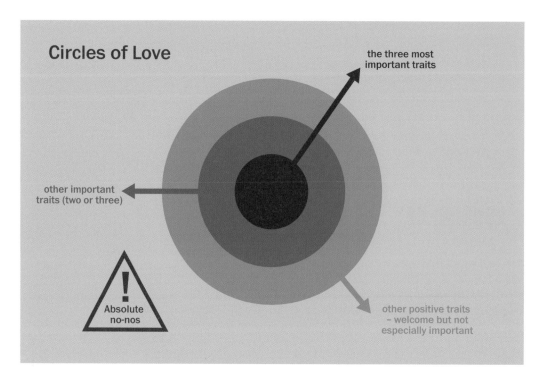

Circles of Love

the three most
important traits

other important
traits (two or three)

!
Absolute
no-nos

other positive traits
– welcome but not
especially important

sense of humour and you're very energetic, and you get together with someone who needs lots of peace and quiet and tends not to laugh about much, you don't have to be psychic to guess that you may have problems. It's sometimes said that opposites attract or that lovers' teasing is a sign of affection, but neither of those statements is generally true in life. In fact, the prospects are far better if you and your partner have certain fundamental characteristics in common. Then, the less important things that you don't share will simply provide a bit of surprise and variety in your relationship without undermining it.

OPTIMISING YOUR SEARCH

While you are marking up the Circles of Love diagram, have a think about what characteristics are important to you in a partner. What kind of person would you like to be with? If you make the effort to work out what you need, that in itself will make you more self-aware, and you'll see things more clearly. You might even find that your dating pattern changes. Perhaps you'll stop always heading for the kind of person who (you know from experience) is not good for you. And in the end, you might just find someone standing right in front of you, smiling – a fantastic, intriguing, great girl or guy who is just what you've been looking for.

STRIPPING OFF

MALE & FEMALE BODIES

WHAT'S THE DIFFERENCE?

Feel like skipping this chapter? You'll be missing something if you do. This is where we take a closer look at the differences between men and women – although these actually amount to far less than people often think. We'll also explain exactly why, as you start to reach sexual maturity, you suddenly feel so different from how you felt before. It's almost as though you are being ambushed by your own body, but don't worry: the more you know about all of this, the easier it is to cope with.

So, we'll begin at the beginning, when you were still in your mother's womb. This is where the differences start to happen. Each parent has two chromosomes, one of which will be passed on to any child they conceive. The mother (XX) can only pass on an X chromosome, but the father (XY) will provide either an X or a Y chromosome. If he contributes a Y chromosome, a boy will eventually be born, and if he passes on an X chromosome, the baby will be a girl. Either way, for the first few weeks, the foetus develops as if it is going to be a girl. Then some time between the sixth and eighth weeks, if the foetus is to become male, something else has to happen. Put simply, this is when a Y chromosome triggers the production of male sex hormones which in turn stimulate the body to develop a penis and testicles.

Much investigation has been done over the last few decades into identifying sex differences in brain organisation, in other words, trying to discover whether male and female brains are wired differently. However, the whole question is very complex. The brain is flexible and ever-changing, and even though structural differences between male and female brains may exist to some degree, our behaviour and feelings are certainly heavily influenced by what we experience and the patterns of information, thought and activity that we learn and repeat. So, for example, many women are capable of impressive spatial thinking and many men have no problem with multi-tasking.

> **The Driver** Testosterone is a hormone – a kind of messenger carrying important information round the body. This sex hormone is produced mainly in the testicles and, to a lesser extent, in the adrenal cortex. In women, much smaller amounts of testosterone are produced, in the adrenal cortex and the ovaries. This hormone is responsible for, among other things, the shape and form of a male body: it creates larger muscles, thicker skin, stimulates the production of facial hair and is responsible for the voice breaking and deepening in adolescence. Above all, it increases libido (sexual desire) in both women and men.

Testosterone does a lot of other things as well. Its precise effect on the foetus is still not entirely understood, but as a boy becomes a man, testosterone influences his behaviour, how he feels, and the strength of his sexual response.

Those first few months in the womb are decisive. The more testosterone you receive, the more masculine you become. Some scientists have taken this idea a step further and think that explanations for transsexuality and homosexuality may be traced back to this stage of development. Their theory is that if a male foetus receives relatively little testosterone, it will be enough for him to develop a penis, but certain parts of his brain will remain 'female'.

Of course, upbringing and environment are also hugely influential, and role models and attitudes in society play a big part in what we consider to be masculine or feminine behaviour. We'll come back to that later.

I like there to be some testosterone in rock, and it's like I'm the one in the dress who has to provide it.
Courtney Love

AUTISM

There has been quite a lot of research into the possibility of a connection between autism and testosterone levels. What prompted these investigations was the fact that boys are four times more likely than girls to be diagnosed with it.

Most people with autism find understanding and relating to other people difficult. Many autistic people lack the intuitive knowledge about how to interact and communicate with others that most of the rest of us take for granted. They struggle to make sense of other people's behaviour, and this can make it extremely difficult for them to react appropriately. Having difficulties with social imagination, though, does not mean that a person lacks either intelligence or imagination: many people with autism are highly creative and may become, for example, accomplished artists, musicians or writers.

If you think, in the broadest terms, about the behaviours and abilities that are traditionally considered to be female and male, you could describe autistic people as lacking female qualities and being overendowed with male characteristics. Testosterone levels might well be responsible for this. And there are some grounds for believing this theory: Professor Simon Baron-Cohen, Director of Cambridge University's Autism Research Centre, discovered that boys and girls who had been oversupplied with testosterone in the womb later developed traits typical of autism. For this reason, the professor regards autism as a manifestation of 'the extreme male brain'. Other researchers pursuing the same theory found that one-year-olds who had received high doses of testosterone in the womb initiated less eye contact with their parents than other children. Speech seems to be affected by testosterone too. At eighteen months old, some studies have found that children exposed to higher than average levels of testosterone in the womb have smaller vocabularies than children exposed to more normal levels. We have to remember, though, that what we learn as we grow up as a result of interacting with the people around us (nurture) is at least as important as what we're born with (nature).

Every boy and every girl has some feminine and some masculine characteristics, and the proportion of one to the other varies from individual to individual. A girl who takes real pleasure in fighting, for example, may have high levels of testosterone that make her likely to behave in what many would regard as a 'masculine' way. But she might also have had a particularly inspiring role model, male or female, who behaved in a way that is conventionally regarded as masculine. Or her behaviour might result from a combination of the two.

What do you think of as typically male or female behaviour? What would you say are your 'masculine' and 'feminine' traits? What kind of balance do you have between the two? Ask your friends or your family how they see you. It can be interesting, anyway, to find out what impression you make on other people.

> **The Secret of the Long Finger** Apparently people with high levels of testosterone have ring fingers that are longer than their index fingers, and not only that, they have large penises too. True or false? Seeing is believing . . .

THE MALLEABLE BRAIN

OK, so people are born one sex or the other with a mixture of masculine and feminine characteristics. But it is not quite as simple as that, thanks to what the brain can do. After birth – and for the rest of your life – it remains flexible. According to what we experience in our lives from babyhood onwards, various connections are made between nerve cells which create information pathways in our brains. The more we learn, the more complex our own personal data-processing systems become. It's a bit like the road network of a city: the bigger the city, the more routes it needs, and the busier these routes become. The great thing is that if these pathways are used repeatedly, they are automatically upgraded and so communication along them becomes faster. And vice versa: unused trails fade away and eventually vanish.

When they are young, children copy the behaviour that they see around them. That's why the way a child is brought up is so important. Kids model themselves on the people they know. Other people provide role models and values that we take on both directly and indirectly from babyhood onwards. This is how we learn what are regarded as masculine and feminine types of behaviour. Our upbringing will also have had a big influence on how masculine or feminine our behaviour is, and on how comfortable we feel with the sexual roles that the rest of society expects us to conform to.

CLOSED FOR REBUILDING

During puberty, a great deal is going on in your brain and your body – it's a bit like a vast building site. In the mid-19th century, the average age for the onset of puberty was between 16 and 17 years old; now it starts significantly earlier. Some girls enter puberty as early as eight years old, and some boys at nine. This means that children now have to cope much earlier with the stresses and strains that go with this stage of development (as do their parents).

At the beginning of this phase, significant changes are occurring in children's brains and bodies as well as in their emotional lives. All of these are inextricably bound up together, which of course doesn't make things any easier. We'll now try to shine a light on some of this confusing stuff.

People forget that the brain is the biggest erogenous zone. *Jackie Treehorn, The Big Lebowski*

Let's start with the brain. Here there's a great burst of activity with renovation and reconstruction happening simultaneously. Remember that network of city streets? During puberty, it is as though the brain's works manager surveys the street layout, identifies routes that were established but hardly ever or never used and closes them off. That is happening all the time – every second of your youth, thousands of nerve connections die out.

But don't worry: at the same time there's a huge amount of activity involving the upgrading and strengthening of other, well-used pathways in parts of the brain that are responsible for decision-making, planning, motivation, the development of a system of values and the ability to put oneself in someone else's position – to empathise. It does mean, though, that it's often confusing and difficult to work out what to think about all sorts of situations, because so much in you is changing. You may find it harder to make decisions, or really difficult to judge whether something is good or bad for you. All of this is very stressful, both for you and for those around you. People get mad at you. Everyone seems to be in a bad mood all the time.

Your parents don't understand why it takes you an hour to decide on the right clothes to wear to school. And you cannot see why they are hurt when you retreat behind your closed door and have almost nothing to say to them. To cap it all, your sleeping habits will probably have changed (although this tends to affect boys more than girls).

112

Suddenly you've become nocturnal, and your day starts about five hours later than everyone else's.

The brain – which is undergoing major reorganisation – is responsible for all of that. Most of the big changes will have happened by the time you're 25, so it's in your teens and early twenties that the confusing effects of changing hormones are at their height. And because the changes going on in the body are different, the effects on boys and girls are not the same. Consequently, this is when male and female experiences really start to diverge.

LADIES FIRST

The brain controls the release of certain hormones. For girls, this means that oestrogen, progesterone and testosterone all come into play. Among other things, these trigger and control a woman's menstrual cycle and are responsible for various other changes in the body.

Growing

Because puberty starts sooner for girls than for boys, their growth spurt also happens earlier. A layer of fat appears just under the skin on the upper arms, breasts, hips, thighs and backside. The pelvis becomes wider – wide enough that a baby could eventually pass through it. These changes produce beautiful womanly curves. Sweat glands become more active, so the body starts to smell different. The seb-aceous glands also work harder and that is what can land you with spots or acne. Spots are the bane of many teenagers' lives. Most will clear up with time, but if you develop serious skin problems, it's worth going to your doctor for help. (One beneficial side effect of the contraceptive pill is that it sometimes improves skin condition.)

Muffin Top! Pizza Face! What? During puberty, your body changes. Girls get called all sorts of unflattering names like fat arse, thunder-thighs, beanpole, skinny minnie, or ironing board (i.e. flat-chested). Tall skinny boys are laughed at and called names like string bean and long streak of piss, others put up with insults like pencil dick or needle dick, and those who have unusually prominent 'man boobs' are teased relentlessly. Name-calling like this can be extremely hurtful, because it makes a person feel as though there is something wrong with them. But in time you will realise that there's absolutely nothing wrong with you. You're fine as you are.

The first body hair starts sprouting in your armpits and around your genital area. Pubic hair in girls eventually makes a roughly triangular shape covering the mons veneris (the soft fleshy mound over a woman's pubic bone) and extends all around the pubic area as far as the anus. Pubic hair is often thicker and curlier than hair elsewhere on your body, and it may be a different colour from the hair on your head.

The swelling of a girl's areolas – the darker areas around her nipples – is the first sign that her breasts are growing. The size and shape of breasts are partly determined by genes. The left breast and its partner on the right often grow at different rates and they may end up being not quite the same size or shape – that's true for one woman in four. Breasts have usually reached their full size by the time their owner is 15 years old, but it can take until the age of 19 for them to be fully developed. Oestrogen levels can affect breast size: if a woman is on the contraceptive pill or is pregnant (when oestrogen levels are high), her breasts will be larger. Also, as you may have noticed, breasts can swell by as much as 20% when a woman is sexually aroused.

Connective tissue in the breasts is responsible for their shape and position or how they hang. Lots of women have stretch marks – even small breasts can develop them if they've grown very rapidly. Breasts are mainly composed of fatty tissue, and when you put on weight, they will get larger. If you lose weight, they'll get smaller again.

A lot of women are dissatisfied with their breasts – which is hardly surprising given the appearance of virtually all the breasts you see in the media. In fact these 'perfect' breasts may well have been covered in makeup to conceal bluish veins, or held in position with adhesive tape so that they sit higher than they would naturally, or treated to some digital retouching. They may even have been under the cosmetic surgeon's knife. You can easily get the impression that all normal breasts are firm and stand straight out from the body, even if they are very large, but that is lies, all lies! The bigger the breasts, the heavier they are. Most large breasts hang down a little from the moment they are fully formed, and this will certainly happen as a woman grows older and the connective tissue in the breast begins to weaken.

Often, the media present the ideal woman's body as very slim with large, firm breasts. This reflects not just men's fantasies but women's too – interestingly, most men and women have the same ideal female body in mind. In reality, though, slim women usually have smaller breasts than those who are more heavily built.

The nipple is the most sensitive part of the breast. If you get cold, or you are aroused, they'll become stiff. Nipples come in all shades from rich reds, through delicate salmon pink to beautiful dark browns. The areola is dotted with very small glands which keep the breast moist when a mother is breastfeeding. These tiny round lumps help the nipple to become erect when it is aroused. It's thought that the reddish nipple and its darker surround make it easy

My breasts have a career. I'm just tagging along.
Pamela Anderson

100 women there, and you didn't invite me. That's 200 breasts! And you kept them all to yourself.
Denny Crane, in Boston Legal

for the baby to locate the right place for suckling. (Don't forget that breasts are designed for feeding babies.)

Boob Jobs, etc The number of cosmetic surgery procedures carried out each year continues to rise worldwide, and the USA and UK are no exceptions to this trend. Data collected by the American Society of Plastic Surgeons has recorded a 500 percent rise in teenage cosmetic surgery in the US over the last fifteen years. The widespread use of airbrushing, plus a lack of diversity in the body types represented in the media means that it is virtually impossible for most people to achieve or maintain the kinds of body we see on TV and in magazines. The YMCA recently conducted a survey in the UK to explore young adults' attitudes around body-image-related issues, looking especially at the impact of images in the media and advertising. More than a third of teenage schoolgirls said they wanted to look like the models in magazines, and breast augmentation was high on their wishlists. Many of the people questioned thought that 'the media and advertisers are still heavily reliant on using ultra-thin or highly muscular body types in advertising and marketing.'

In the USA, a survey carried out by the American Society for Aesthetic Plastic Surgery found that almost half of the breast implant procedures carried out on girls aged 18 and under were for 'purely cosmetic' reasons. It's not unusual in the USA for a girl to be given breast enlargement as a graduation gift or a sixteenth birthday present. Surgery of this kind is less common in the UK, but the number of young women having cosmetic surgical procedures is now rising steadily here too.

There can, of course, be good reasons for having surgery. If, for example, a woman has such heavy breasts that she is suffering from chronic back pain, breast reduction can dramatically improve her quality of life. More often, though, the main reason for having cosmetic surgery is to achieve what the client considers to be a more desirable – even acceptable – look.

I was going to have cosmetic surgery until I noticed that the doctor's office was full of portraits by Picasso.
Rita Rudner

Taking joy in living is a woman's best cosmetic.
Rosalind Russell

It's not just breasts and nipples that start behaving differently when you hit puberty. Other things are happening further down your body that aren't so obvious to other people. A year or two before a girl has her first period, the vagina begins to secrete a liquid substance called cervical mucus. The quantity varies from individual to individual, and it ranges from milky-white to completely transparent. Just before a period, it can be brownish (the first sign of menstrual blood). If you ever have a discharge that is yellow or greenish or that smells bad, consult a health professional: you may have a vaginal infection.

Once a girl has started having periods, the discharge varies according to where she is in her monthly cycle. Just before ovulation, it becomes transparent and stringy. This is the best consistency for sperm to swim through, so be careful. At this point in the month there is a much greater risk that you will fall pregnant if you have sexual intercourse.

Periods

The body produces sex hormones following a cycle that lasts more or less a month (for some women it's a bit longer than this, for others a bit shorter) and generally follows the same pattern. Every 28 days, one of the two ovaries releases an egg – that's ovulation. If the egg isn't fertilised, the lining of the uterus (which has thickened in preparation for a possible pregnancy) comes away and is disposed of through the vagina as menstrual bleeding, otherwise known as a period.

Menstrual bleeding lasts between four and six days. Some women bleed heavily, others have a much lighter flow. People use a lot of different expressions to refer to menstruation: getting your period, that time of the month, Aunt Flo, the curse, the red flag, strawberry week, riding the crimson wave, having your flowers, on the rag, Eve's curse, and an endless number of variations that families and friends use among themselves, including one of the most original posted anonymously online by an American teenager: 'My friends and I call it shark week because a shark's brain is shaped similarly to a uterus.' The timing of a girl's first period varies a lot. You can get it as early as 9 years old, or as late as 15 or even older. In the UK, the average age for first menstruation is 12.9 years. The beginning of menstruation is a sign that you are now able to get pregnant. But if you are sexually active and haven't yet started your periods, make sure that you still use some kind of contraception in case you have sex just before your first period arrives (which will mean that you have ovulated two weeks earlier). And don't forget that you need to protect yourself against infection as well as pregnancy. The best way of coping with both risks is to use a condom (see pages 209-218 for more information on protection).

The Monthly Cycle

Day 1 The day when you start to bleed is the first day of your new cycle. So the first day of bleeding = day 1. It's important to know this if you want to work out when you'll get your next period and when you are likely to be ovulating.

Days 1 to 14 Certain hormones cause an egg in one of your ovaries to ripen. The top layer of the womb lining becomes thicker so that, if the egg is fertilised, it can implant itself there.

Ovulation This happens around day 14 of your cycle. The ripe egg sets off from one of the ovaries down the Fallopian tube next to it and, whether or not it is fertilised, lands in the womb. The egg is viable for only 12 to 18 hours from ovulation, but if you have sex up to several days before, you could still fall pregnant. This is because sperm can survive for up to 72 hours (although in exceptional cases they have been known to last as long as seven days) and fertilise the egg on its way through one of the Fallopian tubes. So beware: ovulation doesn't necessarily happen exactly when you expect it, especially when you have recently started to have periods. Calculating your 'safe' time on the assumption that you can depend on exact dates is not a reliable method of contraception.

Days 14 to 28 If the egg isn't fertilised as it travels down the Fallopian tube, it dies. The top layer of the womb lining detaches itself, and bleeding starts. As levels of one hormone fall, this change stimulates the production of another hormone, and the cycle begins again.

A Woman's Lot

So far we've just been talking about the technical details of the menstrual cycle. But there's also a range of other things that happen, some pleasant, others less so. Some women experience very little discomfort, but for others two points in the cycle can be painful: the period itself and ovulation. Just before and/or during a period, your breasts can become swollen and tender and you may get abdominal cramps, which, if you're unlucky, can be quite severe. Ovulation, around the midpoint of the cycle, can cause aching and tenderness in the abdomen – so-called mittelschmerz (literally 'middle pain' in German). If you suffer badly from pain at either or both of these times, have a chat with a health professional about it. You may be advised to go on the contraceptive pill, as it can ease the painful side effects of the menstrual cycle as well as reduce the build-up of mucous membranes in the womb which in turn means that you produce less blood (heavy bleeding can be quite a problem for some women). Otherwise, relaxation exercises may help, or just moving around – getting your circulation going can ease cramps. Various herbal teas can be beneficial, and there's always the good old hot water bottle.

Let's look at what may happen to your weight. Maybe yesterday you weighed 68 kilos; today the scales say 70 kilos, and you feel bloated. This is normal when you are ovulating, because your body tends to retain more fluid. You may experience similar bloating just before your period. Some women suddenly crave types of food that they wouldn't normally want at all. Don't worry: you'll soon be back to normal.

Monthly Blues

During a woman's cycle, the levels of oestrogen, progesterone and testosterone go up and down at different rates. These shifts can affect mood, libido (sexual desire) and how well you cope with life in general. What most people don't realise is that you can use these variations to your advantage. And that applies to men too: if you are familiar with your partner's cycle, you'll know when in the month she tends to feel particularly sexy and when she is more likely to be grumpy or moody.

If you look at when the highest concentrations of hormones occur, you can see that the cycle divides into two halves: the first runs from the start of bleeding to ovulation, and the second follows on from this and lasts until the first day of the next menstruation. So bleeding happens in the first half, even though the biological changes that set it off occur at the end of the second half. Some women prefer the first half of the month, others the second; some are not aware of any difference between the two. That may sometimes be to do with being on the pill, which dampens down all hormonal effects.

A woman lives with this cycle for a long time – from the start of her first period to the menopause (which usually happens sometime between her mid-forties and early fifties, though it can arrive earlier). The fluctuations in hormone levels can have vastly differing effects on different people. Some women are severely affected by them, others are scarcely aware that anything is happening.

The first half of the cycle comprises weeks one and two. During this time, rising levels of oestrogen make women want to be with other people more, and they feel more outgoing and sociable. They tend to be more relaxed and less critical than at other times as well as enjoying intimacy and closeness. And they're more keen to have sex, especially just before ovulation, which is also when their testosterone levels spike.

Just before ovulation is when oestrogen levels are at their highest. This works on the brain a bit like fertiliser on plants: the brain becomes more active and there is a slight increase in thought activity, producing clearer thinking and a better memory. Ideas come thick and fast, and thought processes tend to be more flexible than at other times.

The second half of the cycle covers weeks two and three. Progesterone levels are rising and they're working against the effects of oestrogen. The brain's activity alters, and the woman becomes fractious and finds it harder to concentrate.

In the last few days of the cycle (just before bleeding starts), progesterone levels fall again and at this point women become even more irritable, often just wanting to be left alone. A lot of girls are familiar with the miserable moods that descend on them a few days before a period. And maybe some young men have noticed that their girlfriend is not great to be around at this time of the month. If a girl has a really extreme version of this effect, she should get help from her doctor. It's likely that she is suffering from PMS (pre-menstrual syndrome). All sorts of situations can quickly become far more difficult on these days than they normally would be. If there are important decisions to be made, it's not a bad idea to wait until you are feeling better.

Because their levels of oestrogen and progesterone (which keep testosterone in check) are both sinking, most women feel the effects of testosterone in their system just before a period: they may be more aggressive and feel keener on sex, even though – by comparison with men – their testosterone levels are relatively low.

Vagina, Vulva *et al*

Many people use the word 'vagina' to describe all the female sex organs, but this is, in fact, inaccurate. What you can see on the outside is the vulva, and inside the vulva is the vagina. The vulva is made up of inner and outer labia (or lips), the opening to the urethra (pee hole), the clitoris, and the hymen (sometimes referred to as a 'cherry', hence 'losing your cherry' meaning losing your virginity).

In porn movies and porn magazines, we see only a very limited selection of vulvas. Most of them will have small, pink, symmetrical lips, with little or no sign of the inner labia protruding between the outer labia (although this is very common in real life). Every last hair has usually been removed, and anything that looks unusual or wrinkled is retouched, bleached or even tattooed to look lighter.

You can only really appreciate how different vulvas are in real life if you see lots of them together. As a response to the misinformation about female sex organs purveyed by the porn industry, various publications have recently appeared that include images showing what they really look like. You could look at *Pussypedia* on www.rfsu.se or *A Whole Book of Beautiful Diverse Vaginas (Vulvas!)* on jezebel.com.

If you haven't yet seen your own vulva, use a mirror to view it. Ask your boyfriend how he would describe it and what he thinks about it.

There are all sorts of 'intimate hygiene' products for sale, but it's best to use only water to wash your vulva, or a soap-free washing lotion. The vagina normally secretes a clear or whitish substance that helps to keep it clean. Don't wash the vagina at all: left to itself, it maintains a healthy, slightly acidic environment that will be disturbed by the use of soap (which is alkaline), and will make you more vulnerable to infection.

		Melonen **melons**			
		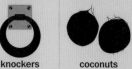			
bust		*Möpse* **pugs**	*Tüten* **bags**		
knockers	**coconuts**	*Hupen* **horns**	*Glocken* **bells**	*une paire de pastèques* **pair of melons**	*une paire des ballons* **pair of balloons**
melons	**jugs**	*Euter* **udder**	*Holz vor der Hütte* **log pile**	*la boîte à lait* **milk carton**	*les lolos* **milkies**	*tronco* **trunk/stump**

━━━━━━━━━━━━━━ **BREASTS** ━━━━━━━━━━━━━━

English	**German**	**French**	**Italian**

━━━━━━━━━━━━━━ **VAGINA** ━━━━━━━━━━━━━━

pussy	**crotch**	*Muschi* **pussy**	*Loch* **hole**	*la figue* **fig**	*la minette* **mine**	*fessura* **slit**
slit	**beaver**	*Liebeshöhle* **love cave**	*Ritze* **crack**	*la moule* **mussel**	*le panier* **basket**	*pozzo* **well, shaft**
bearded clam	**tunnel of love**	*Schnecke* **snail**		*la pâquerette* **daisy**	*la chatte* **cat**
				la motte **butter pat**	

Breasts and vagina/vulva

pulmones
lungs

pitones
humps

tetas
teats

escaparate
shop window

mostrador
display cabinet

portakallar
oranges

ayvalar
quinces

poppe
dder, teats

bufira
shock absorber

batony
white rolls

globos
balloons

limones
lemons

farlar
spotlight

karpuzlar
watermelons

━━━ **BREASTS** ━━━

Italian	Russian	Spanish	Turkish

━━━ **VAGINA** ━━━

tana
cave

schschjel
crack

schschjolka
slit

agujero
hole

alcancía
money box

delik
hole

şeftali
peach

buco
hole

lachmatka
curly

machnatka
furry one

almeja
clam

castaña
chestnut

kapı
door

tschjornyj triugolnik
black triangle

concha
shell/oyster

conejo
rabbit

guardapolvo
overcoat

pimiento
pepper

Pubic Coiffure

Why do we have pubic hair? What is it for? Some think that the musky scent of the skin that gathers in the hair attracts the opposite sex. And pubic hair certainly reduces friction (which could make the skin sore) during sexual intercourse.

Whether you shave off your pubic hair completely, leave a thin strip of it or don't touch it at all depends on what is fashionable and, in the end, on personal taste. It's up to each individual which intimate hairstyle you choose for yourself or whether you prefer to avoid hair removal altogether and enjoy your bush as it is – *au naturel*. Some people think that the porn industry is responsible for the fashion for intimate shaving. Others reckon that the smoothly shaven body image currently so popular in Europe spread from America in the 1980s as a result of fashions for ever more revealing swimwear.

In fact, fashions for shaving the pubic area have come and gone for thousands of years: there are many examples from across history of the hairless body being considered an ideal of beauty. In Ancient Egypt, upper-class women made sure that the only hair on their bodies was on their heads, and the Ancient Greeks adopted a similar ideal of smoothness. Islam has a long history of pubic hair removal, and the Crusaders brought the practice back to medieval Europe where women have removed pubic hair ever since, even when outward morality has dictated otherwise. In Japan, on the other hand, untouched hair round the sexual organs is a sign of fertility, and is considered to be sexually alluring.

If you ask young people today what they think of body hair, you will most often get the answer that it's 'just disgusting', but there are some who find it decidedly unerotic for adults to have the hairless appearance of children 'down there'. Lots of people shave their pubes because they think that it feels better and smoother when they have sex. You definitely get to see a lot more. Shaved pubic areas glimpsed in the shower after sport make it a lot easier to see the infinite variety of ways in which people are built, and for that reason, some sex educators see pubic hair removal as a positive step for women, as their 'hidden' sexual organs become that bit more visible as a result.

There can be downsides to hair removal in this delicate area, though. The skin in the pubic area is very sensitive. If you want to shave, make sure you use a clean, sharp razor and very mild shaving soap so as to avoid razor burn and allergic reactions, and when you're done, apply a soothing anti-inflammatory cream. You can also try waxing, but it isn't that easy to do on your own. Ask a close friend to help you or go to a beauty salon or waxing studio. You can select which shaving style you want to go for from a list of treatments: it might be a Brazilian Landing Strip, which removes all but a narrow strip of hair on the pubis, or a Full Brazilian (aka Hollywood, Bald

Soft and sweet and shaped like a triangle
Some girls want no shape and they shave it all
That's so whack, it hurts with the stubble
Walkin' round and look like an eight-year-old.
Amanda Palmer, Map of Tasmania

You have a lot of nerve telling me to get a wax. If you were in Aruba the natives could bead your back. And it's not just there; every time I blow you I feel like I'm flossing.
Samantha, in Sex & the City

Beaver or German Wax) which will leave you completely hairless. Whichever style you choose, you'll need to repeat the treatment every three or four weeks, depending on your hair type. This is pretty arduous, especially in winter, when you are less likely to bare your body in public. A recent online poll of women in the UK revealed that just over half don't shave their pubic areas, of whom 62% had discovered that their partners preferred the natural look, and 45% could no longer be bothered to keep up pubic grooming. For her appearance in the sixtieth anniversary issue of *Playboy* magazine, the supermodel Kate Moss went full frontal but not fully waxed. Perhaps the tide is turning?

Vagina

The inner sexual organs start from the vaginal opening and they are: the vagina itself, the clitoris, the urethra, female prostate (G-zone – see page 128), the pelvic floor muscles and other erectile areas, in other words, areas that can become sexually aroused.

Why do people say 'Grow some balls'? Balls are weak and sensitive. If you really wanna get tough, grow a vagina! Those things take a pounding.
Betty White

The vagina consists of a muscular, tube-shaped organ about 12 cm long. Some people think that the vagina is just a small hollow or a round hole, but it's much more than that. Think of a long, uninflated balloon. It's flexible and very stretchy, and when it is aroused, the uterus retracts a bit to make more space for it. So you don't need to be scared of thick or long penises: the vagina can accommodate more or less any shape. It can also wrap itself around smaller models, so boys who don't have particularly large penises need have no worries: they can give as much satisfaction to their partners as the next man.

Labia

The labia start growing and changing from the onset of puberty. In some women their surface is smooth; in others, it has a more wrinkled or curvy appearance. Sometimes the inner labia are longer than the outer ones, sometimes they are completely hidden by the outer labia. They come in all shades from light pink to dark brown and are as variable as shells on a beach. Sometimes there is a build-up of a whitish or cream-coloured substance between the inner and outer labia (and/or just inside the vagina) that has a distinctive smell. This is smegma, a natural lubricant made up of dead skin cells, oil secretions and moisture including sweat. If it bothers you (some people find the smell exciting, some not), just rinse it away with warm water. If you still have a bad-smelling discharge after regular washing, it's best to get checked out in case you have an infection.

Hair removal

Which parts of the body
do young women and
men shave, and why?

Parts of the body
from which hair
is removed by
18- to 25-year-olds
as percentages

men

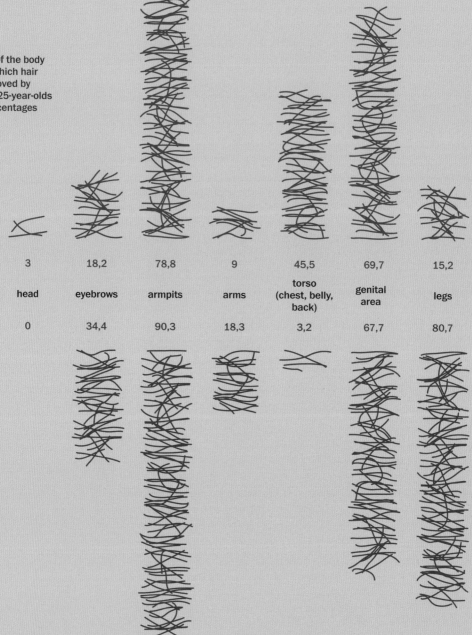

	head	eyebrows	armpits	arms	torso (chest, belly, back)	genital area	legs
men	3	18,2	78,8	9	45,5	69,7	15,2
women	0	34,4	90,3	18,3	3,2	67,7	80,7

women

Results of a German
study carried out in 2009
(no equivalent data in UK)

men

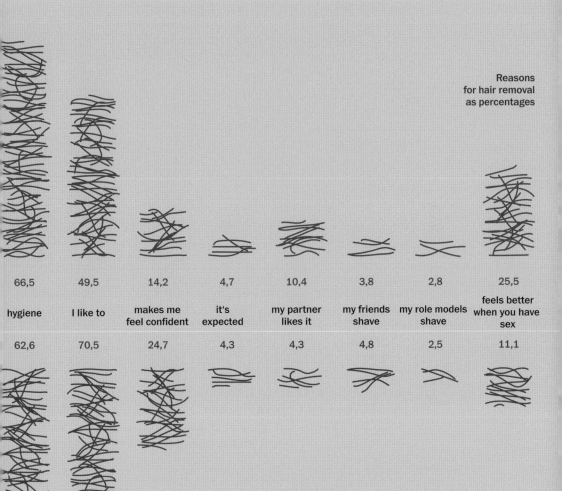

Reasons
for hair removal
as percentages

66,5	49,5	14,2	4,7	10,4	3,8	2,8	25,5
hygiene	I like to	makes me feel confident	it's expected	my partner likes it	my friends shave	my role models shave	feels better when you have sex
62,6	70,5	24,7	4,3	4,3	4,8	2,5	11,1

women

Hymen

The hymen, one of the outer sex organs, is a thin membrane that may just surround the vaginal opening or partially cover it. All hymens have a naturally elastic opening (or openings) that will eventually allow menstrual blood and other discharges to flow safely out of the vagina. A lot of girls are born without one at all.

In some cultures, it can cause a lot of trouble for a woman if on her wedding night it is suspected that her hymen is not intact or is absent, as this is regarded as proof that she has already had penetrative sex. A bloodstain on the bed sheet after the first night of marriage was traditionally taken in many societies as a welcome sign of virginity. That idea is nonsense – the absence of this little flap of skin does not prove whether or not sexual intercourse has happened. However, even now, in some cultures the belief in a complete hymen as both proof and symbol of virginity is so strong that increasing numbers of women are submitting themselves to surgery – hymenoplasty – to replace or create a hymen.

In most women, the hymen opens up when a woman first has sexual intercourse and doesn't bleed. Because all girls' hymens develop differently, how much pain they experience the first time they have sex – or whether it hurts at all – also varies. You can ease, or even completely avoid, any potential pain by gently massaging the vaginal opening with your fingers from time to time, which will stretch the hymen a little.

Clitoris

At the beginning of this chapter, we explained that, early on, a foetus's basic equipment is female. It's only when male hormones arrive on the scene that the male components begin to take shape. So it's perhaps not surprising that female and male sex organs are not as different as many people think. Just like the penis, the clitoris appreciates being stroked, it likes pressure and it enjoys rhythmic movement.

The clitoris is pure in purpose. It is the only organ in the body designed purely for pleasure.
Eve Ensler, The Vagina Monologues

The outer, more visible part of the clitoris consists of the clitoris glans (roughly the same size as a pea) and the foreskin of the clitoris. These are located at the junction between the inner labia, just above the urethra. How far they are from the vaginal opening varies from person to person. That's the part of the clitoris that most people know about. But it is actually a much bigger organ, measuring up to 10 cm and reaching deep inside the labia: the shaft of the clitoris, topped by the glans, curves and then divides into two long legs or roots that run along each side of the pubic bone inside the labia. Scholars in ancient Greece and Rome were aware of the similarity between the clitoris and the penis, but this knowledge was doubted and lost many times over the centuries by male anatomists.

126

The clitoris is a complex organ, and for many women the clitoral glans is the most important stimulation point for achieving an orgasm. Small wonder, as it boasts 8,000 nerve endings by comparison with about 2,500 in the penis, making it even more sensitive. That's why it's important to handle it cautiously during sex. So be gentle with it. Wetting your finger with some saliva will make the touching all the more pleasant. How much pressure or friction is needed varies greatly from woman to woman.

> **The Discovery of the Clitoris** In the mid 16th century an Italian anatomist, Realdo Colombo, identified the clitoris as a woman's 'seat of delight', but the information was largely forgotten until the end of the 20th century. It was not until very recently that female scientists realised the true significance of the clitoris.
>
> In 1987 the American psychologist Josephine Lowndes Sevely published a study in which she identified the clitoris as the original organ from which the penis developed. In the late 1990s, the Australian urologist Helen O'Connell published her description of the clitoris, revealing it to be a far more extensive organ than had been assumed by the modern medical profession and showing how it is connected to the vagina and the prostate.
>
> If you think how far science has advanced, it is pretty extraordinary that proper research into this organ, which is so central to female sexuality, did not happen until the end of the 20th century. This knowledge has far-reaching consequences for the understanding of female sexuality as well as bringing substantial medical benefits. Only now has it become clear exactly where it is safe to make incisions during pelvic surgery so as to avoid destroying the internal structure of the clitoris.

Prostate

Men have a turbo-charge button for sex called the prostate. And so do women. It isn't really a button, of course, but a whole area of arousal that has still not been thoroughly researched and has for a long time been overshadowed by the idea of the G-spot.

Not only did Realdo Colombo identify the clitoris, he also recorded the existence of the female prostate. And, in the 17th century, a Dutch doctor and researcher (Regnier de Graaf) linked this erogenous zone in the vagina with the male prostate. But because nobody knew exactly how the female prostate worked, its existence was largely ignored by doctors. Now, thanks to 20 years of work on the subject published in 2001 by the Slovak Dr Milan Zaviacic, it is clear that the female prostate is a fully functioning organ. So now it's official: the female prostate exists!

127

The female prostate is smaller than the male prostate, but longer. It lies around two to five centimetres inside the front wall of the vagina – towards the abdominal wall around the urethra. That's why, if any pressure is applied to it, some women feel an urge to urinate. The prostate has a slightly ridged surface and is made up of about 40 glands and ducts – three times as many as in the male prostate. These produce an ejaculate which travels along the ducts through the gland tissue to the urethra, which is how a woman, too, can ejaculate.

Some women can actually see their prostate if they squat, mirror in hand, and bear down slightly. The tissue inside the urethra sometimes protrudes a bit, just as it does when you're weeing. But you can also find it, using your fingers: put your index finger and middle finger together and bend them slightly to make a hooked shape, then insert them into your vagina and gently press upwards.

How does the prostate work? When you're sexually aroused, your prostate swells and fills with liquid, making its normally slightly ridged surface somewhat smoother. In some women, the prostate may feel rather numb, and touching it may be uncomfortable to start with. It might even hurt a bit when touched. That is quite normal, because this is a part of the body that many women are not even aware they possess, and it's as if it hasn't quite come alive yet. If a person is unaware of a part of the body because he or she doesn't know about it, the brain does not associate it with desire or sexual pleasure. But don't worry, it takes only a small amount of practice to turn the prostate into an erogenous zone. Once the prostate is stimulated during sex – with fingers, or a large or curved penis, or with good thrusting technique – you'll probably start having completely new sensations, and your orgasms may be different.

G-zone

The so-called G-spot has been the subject of a lot of controversy. Scientists, sexologists, women and men have argued fiercely about whether this place – which is supposed to give women the most intense orgasms – actually exists. That's because it's not easy to be precise about where it is. It's supposed to be located just past the vaginal opening somewhere along the urethra in the direction of the abdomen, in other words, right in the middle of the glandular tissue of the prostate. If this area is stimulated, it can indeed produce intense orgasms.

It seems very likely that when people talk about the G-spot, what they are actually referring to (without realising it) is the female prostate. It would explain why no-one has been able to quite pin down its exact location, because it isn't one particular place, it's a whole area of highly sensitive tissue. Scientists had, some time ago, discussed the possibility that part of the vagina was especially sensitive, but when the press picked up on the idea, it quickly (and misleadingly) became described as a single, magical 'spot'. In the interests of accuracy, we've decided, in this book, to refer to this area as the G-zone.

Female Genital Mutilation (FGM) Horrifyingly, 125 million women and girls around the world have been subjected to female genital mutilation, and 66,000 women and girls living in Britain. FGM involves girls having part (sometimes all) of their external genitalia cut out without any medical reason. It can consist of: removing all or part of the clitoris, sometimes together with the inner (and even the outer) labia, and/or narrowing the vaginal opening by 'sewing up', leaving only a tiny hole through which a girl can urinate and menstruate. Some girls die. All have to cope with lifelong physical and emotional consequences.

FGM, which is not associated with a particular religion, is most common in parts of the Middle East and Asia and in 28 African countries, but it also happens in immigrant communities in countries where the practices are illegal, such as the UK. Here, it's estimated that over 20,000 girls under the age of 15 are at risk of FGM, although it's hard to get firm figures because of the 'hidden' nature of the crime. Although it is illegal to arrange this, girls are sometimes taken to their countries of origin during school holidays for the procedure. It's even suspected that some families are clubbing together to bring 'cutters' over to the UK. In 2012 the United Nations passed a resolution condemning all female genital mutilation, and the World Health Organisation has described the appalling long-term health problems that it brings. But in common with other organisations trying to stop this terrible practice, it doesn't mention the one effect on girls and women which is probably the reason for FGM being carried out in the first place: the removal of women's capacity for sexual pleasure.

Fertilisation

When a man ejaculates while having sex with a woman, assuming he is not wearing a condom, sperm is deposited in the vagina. The sperm then swim up into the Fallopian tubes, although only 0.1% of them will reach the egg. Sperm are equipped with enzymes that soften the outer layer of the egg, allowing it to be fertilised. Only one sperm will manage to penetrate the egg. Occasionally, a second egg is fertilised by a second sperm and the result is non-identical twins, and, even more rarely, identical twins are born after a single fertilised egg has divided very early on in its development.

Five to seven days later, the fertilised egg implants itself in the wall of the womb and starts to divide and grow. If a fertilised egg fails

It is a well-documented fact that guys will not ask for directions. This is a biological thing. This is why it takes several million sperm cells . . . to locate a female egg, despite the fact that the egg is, relative to them, the size of Wisconsin.
Dave Barry

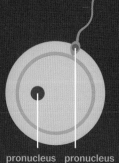

pronucleus of egg   pronucleus of sperm

combining of male and female chromosomes

first dividing stage and separation into two daughter cells

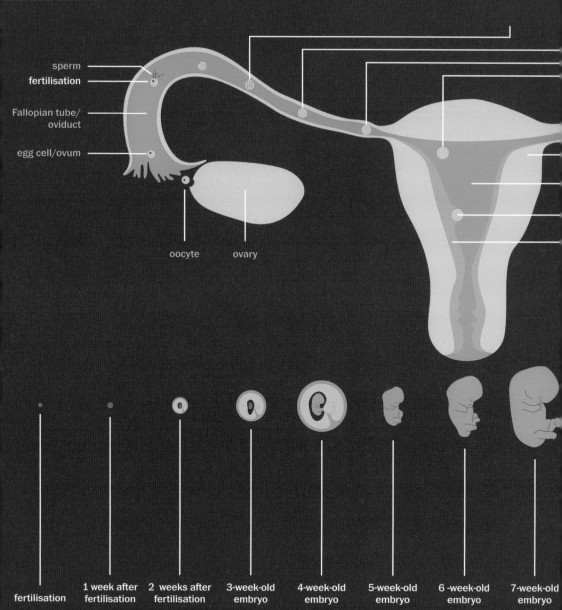

sperm

fertilisation

Fallopian tube/ oviduct

egg cell/ovum

oocyte   ovary

fertilisation

1 week after fertilisation

2 weeks after fertilisation

3-week-old embryo

4-week-old embryo

5-week-old embryo

6-week-old embryo

7-week-old embryo

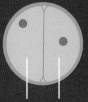

daughter cells
**two-cell stage
around day 2**

**four-cell stage
around day 3**

**morula
day 4**

**blastocyst
day 5**

What happens
after fertilisation?

uterus/womb

uterine cavity

**embryo implants
on day 6 or 7**

lining of the uterus

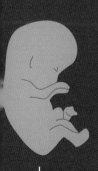

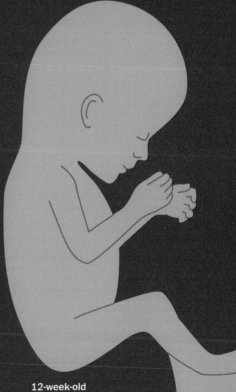

**8-week-old
embryo**

**9-week-old
foetus**

**12-week-old
foetus**

to implant, it will pass out of the body with the next menstruation. So a lot of early-stage pregnancies go unnoticed. Occasionally an egg implants in a Fallopian tube and starts to grow there. This is known as an ectopic pregnancy which will quickly become very painful and needs to be treated fast by health professionals (one probable outcome – a ruptured Fallopian tube – can be very dangerous).

I'm Pregnant – Now What?

If contraceptives are used properly, the likelihood of getting pregnant is pretty slim. But things can go wrong: condoms can be put on incorrectly or break, a diaphragm can be inserted wrongly, and the pill's effectiveness can be reduced if other medication is being taken, if you vomit, or if you have missed even a single dose.

The moment your period is late, worry creeps in: *I couldn't be pregnant, could I?* Whether that is a happy thought or an anxious one will depend on your circumstances. The younger you are, the less likely it is that you'll be pleased by the prospect. Sometimes your period can be late just because your cycle isn't as regular as usual, as a result of stress or other pressures. But it's a good idea to find out as soon as possible why it hasn't arrived – by using a pregnancy test (which you can buy over the counter) or by going to see a doctor. It's understandable that some girls are hesitant about doing the test, because they're so frightened of the consequences if it shows positive. If this is how you feel, it's a good idea to get help from someone you trust or from people who are trained to deal with this kind of situation (see page 250 for contact details).

If you do discover that you are pregnant, and there is a possibility that you might want to have an abortion, don't delay. In general, it's best for abortions to be carried out as early as possible, ideally before the 13th week of pregnancy, and in the UK over 90% of terminations are performed by this time. Abortion law varies from country to country and, in the USA, from state to state. In some American states, performing or receiving an abortion is fenced around with such complex conditions that it is virtually impossible for a woman to have one.

In England, Wales and Scotland, legal termination of pregnancy may be carried out up to 24 weeks provided that two registered medical practitioners agree that 'the continuance of the pregnancy would involve risk, greater than if the pregnancy were terminated, of injury to the physical or mental health of the pregnant woman or any existing children of her family. The woman's actual or reasonably foreseeable future environment may be taken into account.' A young woman under 16 may consent to an abortion without parental knowledge or consent if two doctors agree that she has sufficient maturity and understanding to appreciate what is involved.

How to Do the Sums How do you work out how far along your pregnancy is? Just count the weeks since the first day of your last period – Day 1. This is how the calculation is done, even though fertilisation will not have happened until Day 14. In other words, by the time you realise that your period has not arrived, you could already be four or five weeks pregnant. If you don't notice until a bit later than this, you'll obviously be further on in your pregnancy.

NOW FOR THE BOYS

As explained earlier, a male foetus gets a shot of testosterone in the womb, and during puberty the hormone is boosted again, setting in train some big changes. It is responsible for the growth of body hair, the voice breaking, and powerful sexual urges. And the worst thing is that boys have almost no warning of any of this. For them, puberty arrives practically overnight, and suddenly they don't understand anything anymore. Nothing seems to make sense.

Growing Up

The majority of boys reach puberty between the ages of 10 and 17 years old. Around 13, most of them will have a big growth spurt, when their arms, legs, feet and penis all get much bigger. The rest of the body lags behind a bit, and it's only about a year later that it catches up, hence that lanky look that adolescent boys often have. It's only by about 19 years old that their bodies finish growing, by which stage their shoulders and chests are noticeably broader. It takes a few more years for the changes to bone and muscle density to be completed.

Testosterone increases the proportion of lean muscle to body fat. Muscles become more visible and prominent. The skin becomes thicker and greasier, which can lead to spots or even acne – the result of the sebaceous glands being stimulated by testosterone and producing more sebaceous oil. Four out of five young men develop blocked pores, which are perfect breeding grounds for bacteria. As testosterone plays a big part in blocked pores, boys tend to suffer from them more than girls. If you have a serious case of spots or acne, it's a good idea to go to your doctor for advice and treatment. Armpits, genitals and feet all produce sweat and smells that you've never had before. How noticeable the smell is depends on your personal hygiene. A faint whiff can even be a turn-on for some women.

Body Hair

The first pubic hair usually appears at the base of the penis. From there it spreads out towards your belly button and thighs. Armpit

Female and male sex organs

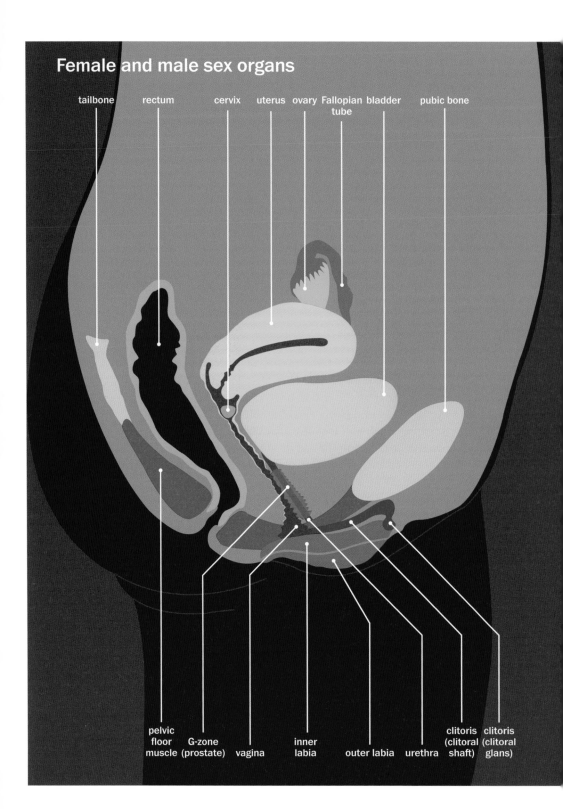

tailbone   rectum   cervix   uterus   ovary   Fallopian   bladder   pubic bone
tube

pelvic
floor
muscle   G-zone   inner   clitoris   clitoris
(prostate)   vagina   labia   outer labia   urethra   (clitoral   (clitoral
shaft)   glans)

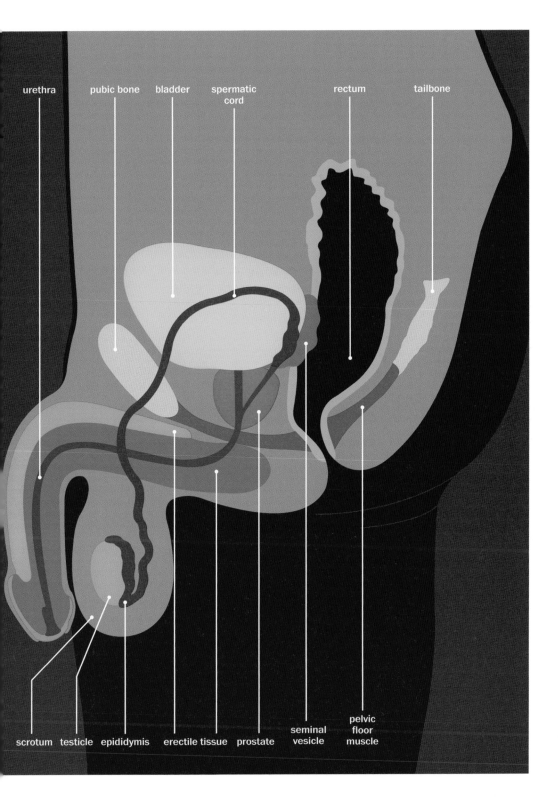

urethra · pubic bone · bladder · spermatic cord · rectum · tailbone

scrotum · testicle · epididymis · erectile tissue · prostate · seminal vesicle · pelvic floor muscle

hair and hair elsewhere on your body, including your chin, starts growing about two years later.

Body hair is usually coarser than the hair on your head. If you really don't like it, you can remove it with a razor and shaving foam. But don't shave against the direction of growth or you're likely to get razor burn. Hair can also be removed by waxing, but that is quite painful and not for everyone. You may prefer the natural look, or just to do a bit of light trimming – it is entirely a matter of personal taste.

Breaking Voice

When he is about 15 years old, a boy's voice starts to 'crack' or 'break'. Testosterone stimulates growth in the larynx (the voice-box), the vocal chords thicken and the Adam's apple is formed. While your voice is breaking, you may well make strange squeaky noises completely involuntarily, which can sound very amusing – to others, that is. The process lasts only a few months.

Penis, testicles and scrotum

Between eleven and a half and fifteen years of age, a boy's testicles, and then his penis, grow larger. You'll find that sometimes your penis will become hard without any direct sexual stimulus – sometimes in completely inappropriate circumstances. Embarrassingly, it can seem to have a mind of its own.

You'll ejaculate for the first time – meaning you'll produce your first drops of semen – about a year after the onset of puberty. You are now a fertile male. Sometimes you may wake up having ejaculated in your sleep: this is called a wet dream, and it's completely normal. Testosterone levels spike between 4 am and 5 am, and sometimes you may wake with a hard-on as a result. This just shows that everything is functioning normally. If you don't jerk off, your erection will disappear after you get up, and certainly by the time you go for your morning pee.

To get down to basics: penises come in many different sizes and shades. The shortest functional human penis so far recorded was 1.5 cm long, referred to as a micropenis because it measured less than 7 cm. The guy currently credited with owning the longest penis in the world has one that measures 20.3 cm when flaccid and 34.3 cm when erect.

The size of a penis is determined by genes and by how much testosterone was received by the embryo in the womb. Penises can be anything from a pale reddish colour to almost black. Some have an almost bluish look (from the veins lying just below the surface of the skin) and get even darker on arousal when the blood supply increases.

Lots of boys are dissatisfied with the appearance of their penis. Maybe one reason for this is that they've viewed their dad or grandfather naked and have seen how much larger their genitals are. The porn industry and the media – which are obsessed with size – don't help either. Unsurprisingly, men with larger than average penises are always chosen to act in porn movies, although only one man in a hundred actually has a 'porn penis' (20 cm or more).

Measured from the pubic bone to the glans, the erect penis length of Europeans varies between 11 cm and 17 cm, so the average is 14.27 cm long, very similar to the average for North American men; the length of a flaccid penis varies from 7 to 10 cm long (average 8.3 cm). Asian penises tend to be slightly smaller, and the average African penis is a bit larger. It is interesting that while penis length is the subject of seemingly endless fascination, and therefore surveys, there are no equivalent studies of the sizes of female genitalia.

Of course length is not the whole story, the thickness of the penis also counts. In fact, as far as the woman's enjoyment is concerned, girth matters more than length. A thick penis can be very exciting as it presses against the vaginal wall. But if it is too big in diameter to be comfortable, a lubricating cream or gel will help. Some penises can virtually double in size when erect, whereas others don't get much bigger. So a limp penis tells you very little about how big it can become. In any case, it's not about size, it's about how you use what you've got.

It's worth remembering that most men view their own penis from above, and the foreshortening effect if you see it from this angle is bound to make yours look shorter than the penises of the other guys standing nearby in the shower. Women, however, usually see it from the front or from underneath, from where it looks significantly bigger. And you can also make use of an optical illusion: if the pubic hair is trimmed quite short, or shaved off, the penis tends to look longer. Lots of people will find it more pleasant when kissing you or giving you head not to get hair in their mouths. The shape of the rest of your body has an effect too: in young men carrying a lot of weight, part of the penis can actually retract into the body, becoming enveloped in fat, so that only a small section of it still protrudes. Sport, exercise and a healthy diet can transform the situation.

In some sex positions, a small penis can be more comfortable for a woman. It can be quite painful if a penis is so long that some thrusts reach as far as the cervix. And it takes careful practice to manage anal sex successfully with a large penis. Many people would agree that in this situation, small is beautiful.

You'll have to forgive my brother. He thinks with his penis, and his penis isn't very bright.
Alan Harper, in Two and a Half Men

Look at all the things that can go wrong for men. There's the nothing-happening-at-all problem, the too-much-happening-too-soon problem, the dismal-droop-after-a-promising-beginning problem; there's the size-doesn't-matter-except-in-my-case problem, the failing-to-deliver-the-goods problem . . . and what do women have to worry about? A handful of cellulite? Join the club. A spot of I-wonder-how-I-rank? Ditto.
Nick Hornby, High Fidelity

> **Bent Dicks** Sometimes the erectile tissue in a penis fills with different amounts of blood in different places, and then the penis bends over to one side. But don't worry: many women know that a slightly curved penis can produce a more stimulating experience than a straight one. A few men have penises that are so curved that intercourse may be painful and either difficult or impossible. If this happens to you, consult a doctor. It could be that you are suffering from a treatable condition called Peyronie's disease.

Glans

In an uncircumcised penis, you see the glans or tip only when it is fully erect or when the foreskin is pulled back. The head of the penis is composed of the same erectile tissue as the urethra and ends at the corona (the rim of the glans). In 10% of men, this ridge of sensitive tissue is dotted with tiny raised white points (the scientific name for them is *Hirsuties papillaris genitalis*). They have nothing to do with sexual activity or personal hygiene and are completely harmless.

The glans is equipped with about 2,500 nerve endings and so is highly sensitive and very responsive to being touched and caressed. Another interesting place for kissing and licking is the seam of skin (the penile frenulum) connecting the foreskin to the underside of the glans.

Foreskin

The foreskin, which protects the highly sensitive glans or head of the penis, is a double-layered sheath of skin and mucous membrane. The two layers are not fused together but lie one on top of the other, so they can move independently. The inner surface of the foreskin is covered in minute glands that release a creamy substance. This keeps the foreskin and the glans soft and slippery and allows the foreskin to glide back and forth without friction. It's under here, at the join between the glans and the shaft, that smegma (consisting of dead skin cells, skin oils and moisture) can gather: a whitish or cream-coloured substance sometimes referred to as knob cheese or cock cheese. It's important to clean this area carefully on a daily basis, by pulling the foreskin back gently and rinsing with warm water.

Around a third of men in the world have been circumcised. Male circumcision is probably the world's most widely performed procedure, yet it is rare for it to happen for medical reasons. It is part of religious law in Judaism, and commonly practised in Islamic countries and communities. But in other parts of the world it has simply become what is expected to happen to male children, with many parents assuming that it brings health benefits, although there is little or no evidence for this. In the USA and Britain, where, in the 19th century, there were very negative attitudes about sex, and masturbation in particular, doctors used it to prevent or cure 'masturbatory insanity'. In Europe today, male circumcision is performed less and less frequently. In the UK, rates have dropped steadily – now only around 8% of boys under the age of 15 have the procedure. But around 75% of American males have been circumcised, and, although rates are slowly dropping, over half of boys born in the USA still undergo the procedure. Circumcision is most prevalent in parts of the Middle East, North and West Africa, and in Bangladesh, Pakistan and Indonesia.

There are various ways of performing a circumcision, but usually the foreskin is pulled over the top of the glans and any part of it that extends beyond the tip of the glans is removed. The cut edge of the foreskin is then cauterised or stitched. The healing process takes about ten days for babies and a bit longer for adults. There is growing controversy about infant circumcision. Some people say that a man's decision to be circumcised is his choice, but that a child cannot possibly give informed consent to an operation that will change his body for life. The foreskin is one of the most sensitive parts of the male body, so removing it obviously removes the possibility of sensation there. And a glans that is out in the open all the time, rather than wrapped in a foreskin, is likely to become less sensitive. This does not, however, stop circumcised men enjoying sex.

Testicles

The testicles are a pair of oval organs about the size of small eggs surrounded by the scrotum, which is a thin-walled, stretchy bag of skin that hangs down beneath the penis. On the outside, a thin seam divides the two sections; on the inside they are separated by a membrane. There are two chambers, one for each testicle.

The scrotum has its own system of temperature regulation, independent from the rest of the body. It's important that the testicles are kept just below body temperature for optimal sperm production. If the scrotum gets too warm, it relaxes so that the testicles hang further away from the body and become cooler. If it's too cold, the scrotum tightens up and the testicles are held closer to the warmth of the rest of the body. You've probably already noticed this happening. If you are unwell, with a high temperature, your scrotum will hang lower than usual. And if you go for a dip in cold water, it raises itself higher.

Each testicle contains a system of tiny tubes where sperm are produced and nourished; they take about 45 days to come to maturity. Each testicle is capable of producing up to 150 million sperm per day. The testicles also produce testosterone, which drives sexual desire. They usually hang at slightly different heights – an ingenious design feature, ensuring that the testicles are never so close together that they squash each other.

. . . And if you play with the balls, the penis likes that. It's kind of fun. But we did find out one negative thing about balls. If you hit them really hard . . . it's a total system reset.
Robin Williams

Scrotum

Just like the penis, scotums come in many different shapes, sizes and colours. Some are light brown, others salmon pink, some really dark. Some are firm little sacks, others are loose, dangling pouches.

Semen

People often think that what squirts out during ejaculation is all sperm, but it isn't. It's a mixture of sperm (thick and milky) and liquids from the seminal vesicles and the prostate gland (watery and transparent) which provide the method of transport for the sperm. As it is rich in fructose (a sugar), it is also a source of energy for the sperm. That's why sperm can survive for up to a week inside a woman.

Each ejaculation contains two to six millilitres of sperm, and each millilitre contains 50 to 150 million spermatozoa. That sounds like a lot, but it amounts to only about a teaspoonful. In porn movies you often see huge amounts of semen spraying out over the woman, but it's fake and has nothing to do with normal quantities of ejaculate.

Sometimes, if you haven't ejaculated for a while, there may be a bit more than usual. And a good quantity is often produced after long and intensive foreplay. Often sperm can spurt out and land 20 or 25 centimetres away. At other times it will just dribble out.

Healthy ejaculate can be white, grey or yellowish. Sometimes it's liquid, sometimes more like jelly. If it's light pink, that could indicate the presence of blood and you should get yourself checked by a doctor.

The basic taste of semen is slightly metallic, but this can be affected by what has been eaten. Foods that improve its flavour include: fruit and fruit juices (because of the sugars), especially lemons and limes, as well as mint, coriander, parsley and green tea. Foods that are better avoided are asparagus, meat, garlic, onions, broccoli, cauliflower, red cabbage, strong oily spices, coffee and chocolate. These will definitely have an impact on the provider of a blowjob. You'll be doing your lover a favour if you ease up on the spicy foods.

Urethra

The opening at the top of the glans leads into the urethra, through which semen and urine flow – not at the same time, of course. That's why it can be so hard to pee when your penis is erect.

Perineum

This is the name for the area between the scrotum and the anus which is equipped with a lot of nerve endings. The seam or ridge in the middle of it is called the perineal raphe (which extends all the way along the underside of the penis, through the middle of the scrotum and along the perineum towards the anal opening). Some men find it exciting to be stimulated in this area, particularly if gentle pressure is applied, although others find it does little or nothing for them.

Anus
The anus is the opening at the end of the rectum which is the passage from the bowel. Rich in nerve-endings, it is rosette-shaped, highly sensitive and swells during sexual arousal. (More information about anal sex on pages 161-162.)

Prostate
This gland produces almost a quarter of the liquid in ejaculate. The rest of the liquid comes from the seminal vesicles nearby. Just before ejaculation, the prostate pushes fluid into the urethra to join the sperm. Some men describe this feeling as a pulling sensation reaching right back to the testicles, while others say that the testicles themselves feel as though they are full of pressurised liquid. And right after this, ejaculation happens. (With a lot of practice, some men can achieve a so-called dry orgasm – reaching a climax without ejaculating.) A lot of men enjoy it if fingers are used to stimulate their prostate from inside the anus. We explain exactly how this can be done on page 162.

Hygiene
From the onset of puberty, your body starts to smell different. Your armpits sweat more, as do your feet and genitals. Sweat, which is slightly salty, helps to prevent your body from overheating. If it stays on the body for any length of time, it produces a very pungent odour.

We've already mentioned smegma on the penis, which can quickly become unpleasantly smelly. So this is where we get bossy about washing: it is really important to wash thoroughly every day. Just use water on your genitals. Soap can easily irritate the sensitive skin in this area and masks the body's natural fragrance. To clean the penis properly, pull the foreskin back and wash the opening to the urethra and all the way round the glans. Then wash the base of the penis and your testicles, as well as any pubic hair. Finally, dry yourself carefully. Many people find the natural fragrance of a clean body erotic and exciting. Others may need a bit of time to get used to it – and to associate it with feeling sexy – before they find it a turn-on.

I've Got to Go! Both men and women can sometimes experience an overwhelming urge to pee during sex. The reason for this lies in increased blood flow and a higher than usual metabolic rate. This makes the kidneys work faster than normal, so the bladder fills up quickly, and you suddenly feel an urgent need to urinate.

English		German		French		Italian
cock		*Schwanz* **tail**				*cazzo* **tail**
tool	prick	*einäugige Schlange* **one-eyed snake**	*Ständer* **stand**	*l'asperge* **asparagus**	*l'engin* **engine**	*canna* **rod**
magic wand	knob	*kleiner Mann* **little man**	*Latte* **lath**	*le dard* **sting**	*le cigare à moustaches* **moustache and cigar**	*pendaglio* **pendant**
one-eyed trouser snake	bone	*Rute* **birch (for beating)**	*Zauberstab* **magic wand**	*le noeud* **knot**	*la queue* **tail**	*stanga* **bar**

──────────────── penis ────────────────

| **English** | | **German** | | **French** | | **Italian** |

──────────────── testicles ────────────────

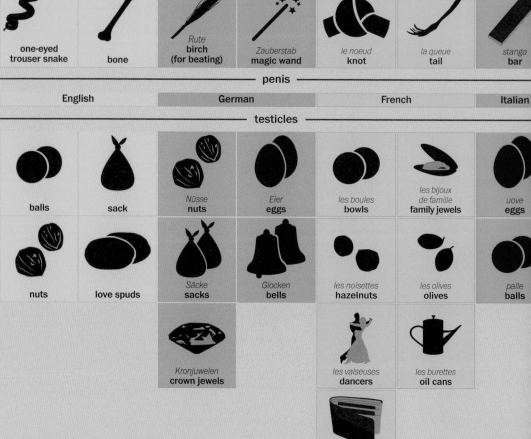

balls	sack	*Nüsse* **nuts**	*Eier* **eggs**	*les boules* **bowls**	*les bijoux de famille* **family jewels**	*uove* **eggs**
nuts	love spuds	*Säcke* **sacks**	*Glocken* **bells**	*les noisettes* **hazelnuts**	*les olives* **olives**	*palle* **balls**
		Kronjuwelen **crown jewels**		*les valseuses* **dancers**	*les burettes* **oil cans**	
				les bourses **purses**		

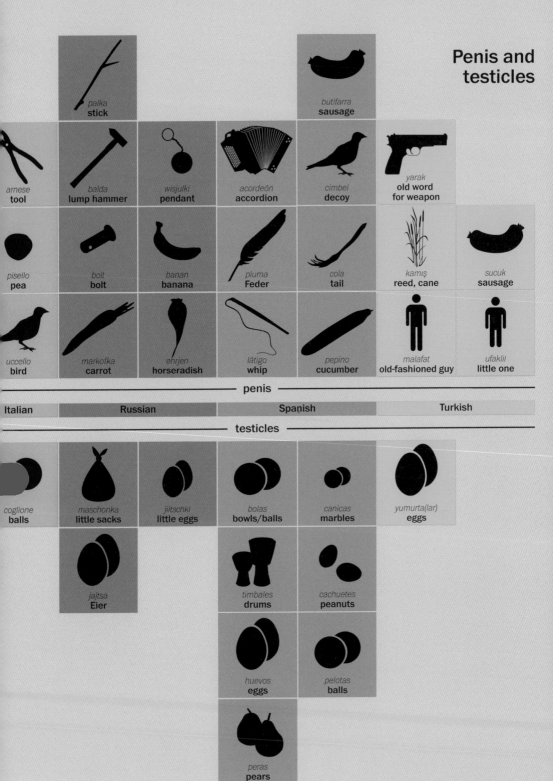

Penis and testicles

	palka **stick**			*butifarra* **sausage**	

arnese **tool** — *balda* **lump hammer** — *wisjulki* **pendant** — *acordeón* **accordion** — *cimbel* **decoy** — *yarak* **old word for weapon**

pisello **pea** — *bolt* **bolt** — *banan* **banana** — *pluma* **Feder** — *cola* **tail** — *kamış* **reed, cane** — *sucuk* **sausage**

uccello **bird** — *markofka* **carrot** — *ehrjen* **horseradish** — *látigo* **whip** — *pepino* **cucumber** — *malafat* **old-fashioned guy** — *ufaklii* **little one**

—— **penis** ——

Italian	Russian	Spanish	Turkish

—— **testicles** ——

coglione **balls** — *maschonka* **little sacks** — *jiitschki* **little eggs** — *bolas* **bowls/balls** — *canicas* **marbles** — *yumurta(lar)* **eggs**

jajtsa **Eier** — *timbales* **drums** — *cachuetes* **peanuts**

huevos **eggs** — *pelotas* **balls**

peras **pears**

BRAVE NEW WORLD

TECHNICAL INFORMATION

TECHNICAL INFORMATION

In sex, there's no right or wrong. What one person loves doing can be a complete turn-off for someone else. That's why it's not possible to write a simple instruction manual for good sex. But there are a few ideas worth passing on, and maybe even a basic formula. It's a bit like getting a simple recipe for pizza dough, and then devising your own topping. You could use classic ingredients or you might prefer a more original combination. One day you might prefer mild, unchallenging flavours, another day something hot and spicy. You can go for lots of ingredients or just a few.

WHO SHOULD BE ON TOP?

Positions for having sex have long been the subject of great fascination. Many people think that if you can have sex in a wide variety of positions, and you switch from one to another all the time, that automatically makes you a fantastic lover. But lots of positions alone do not add up to good sex. Far more important than acrobatic contortions – however broad your repertoire – is what you feel in any particular position: how arousing you and your partner find it, and whether it helps build excitement in both of you. For many men, what's even more important is whether it allows you to contain yourself. Some positions make it almost impossible to delay ejaculation, especially when you are relatively inexperienced. The missionary position, for example, is no help at all with this, even though it's the one that most people tend to stick with.

In this chapter we will tell you about the most important positions and explain who does what and where, as well as how to get the best out of the positions, and what you might find particularly erotic. Some positions are better than others for maximum enjoyment and sensation. Find out how different positions work for you. Try things. Discover what feels good to you. It doesn't matter what other people get up to, or, rather, what you think they get up to.

That girl just asked me to give her my top ten sexual positions; and, after the two that I knew, I just started naming insects . . . The weird thing is, she said she'd already tried 'Stink-bug'.
Elliot, in Scrubs

So to answer what is probably the first question: who should be on top? This is simply a matter of taste. Usually the person on top has more control, and is literally setting the pace. Just being in charge like this can be very exciting for men and women alike. Others prefer a more passive role. In some positions, neither person is on top.

Missionary Position

One of you lies on your back, stretched out on the bed, and the other lies face down on top. The person on top supports some of their body weight on their lower arms. You're lying with your chests, bellies and

genitals touching. What is really nice about this position is that you can look into each other's faces. Seeing your partner getting excited can be really arousing. It's easy to let your eyes wander over your partner's upper body. You can stroke each other, and the person underneath can wind their legs around their partner's.

If the man is on top and puts too much pressure on his lower arms and knees, this can lead to so much muscle tension building up that he comes faster than he wants to. If he tries to stop this happening, and holds his breath at the same time (so there's pressure from the inside too), he's unlikely to last more than a few seconds. It's better to make long, gentle movements and to take deep breaths. Sometimes it works well if the girl is on top to start with. In this position, she can rub her clitoris against him, and move her pelvis around so that she can really feel him inside her. And he can see her breasts swinging above him. Later, when he has had more experience in holding back, they can swap over. And then she will get the chance to move her pelvis against his from beneath him, again so that she can feel him inside her. Just the sight of his penis entering her can be really exciting, and she can gaze at his upper body too.

> **Flexed muscles** Contracting or flexing muscles helps to build excitement, which is why we enjoy tensing muscles when we feel sexy. But the longer you keep this up, the more shallow your breathing will become, and the less good your circulation, and, in the end, you will feel less aroused as a result.

Doggy Style

For this position, she is on all fours (kneeling, with her hands on the bed or floor). For some women, this position expresses real confidence in her partner, as if to signal: 'I'm entirely in your hands: I'm giving myself to you.' This position is good for stimulating the female prostate, the G-zone. Another advantage of the doggy position is that it gives you a great view of your partner's behind, which tends to look especially good from this angle.

He stands or kneels behind her and pushes into her. She can help him by slightly spreading her legs so that her knees are at least as wide apart as her hips, which will make it easy for him to find his way into her. He should enter her gently, making only small movements and ask her whether she likes what he is doing. As he thrusts harder, it's still important to go on checking whether everything is OK for her. She can let him know what she wants by saying 'slower!' or 'deeper!' Then she won't feel so passive, and being told what she wants will make him even more excited.

While thrusting, he can grasp her firmly by the hips. He can bend his body over hers and wrap his arms around her, or touch her breasts or massage her labia or clitoris. At some point, he could take a break from thrusting, and just enjoy being inside her, then make shallow movements in and out or circular movements. Or she can touch herself, cup his testicles in her hand, or gently pull on them.

She could also ask him to pause for a moment. Then he stays inside her but stops moving, and she begins to move instead. When a woman is highly aroused, the sensation of the penis deep inside, gently touching the entrance to the uterus, can be very pleasurable. But, in this position, a long penis making a lot of contact with the cervix can be too much. If this happens, a woman can use her hips to move away from her partner a little or ask him not to thrust so deeply. If it's still uncomfortable, she can control how deep he goes by holding his hips a little away from her with her hands, or by wrapping a silk scarf round the base of his penis – that way it's impossible for him to thrust quite so deeply, and he doesn't even have to think about it.

Cowboy, Cowgirl or Rider

One of you lies stretched out on your back. The other sits on top and guides the penis into the vagina. The person on top uses his shins to steady himself on the bed and moves as though bouncing up and down in the saddle, rotating his hips or tilting his pelvis backwards and forwards. The contrast between relaxing and tensing muscles that you get with this tipping movement can feel great – a bit like being carried along on waves. If the woman is on top, she can really be in charge of her excitement, because she can control the pressure or friction on her clitoris or stimulate herself. And by moving her pelvis at the same time, she can increase her enjoyment even more. He can also massage her clitoris, whether he's on top or not. She should gently guide his hands to where she wants them, or tell him what to do. Don't be surprised if, in this position, the penis slips out of the vagina: this can easily happen, depending on how long and/or hard it is. Finally, the whole experience can be even more intense if you keep your movements slow and vary the rhythm from time to time.

Frog

The basic position for the frog is the same as for the rider except that the person on top doesn't rest on his or her shins, but squats, feet on the mattress, over the sex organs of the other person. This delivers a bit more bounce than you get in the rider position. Anyway it often produces a rapid up- and-down movement not unlike the effect for a guy of jerking off. If you want to do this movement slowly (which will produce more pleasure), you'll need sports-level stamina, good thigh muscles and a very mobile pelvis. But it's well worth the effort!

Spoons

This is called the spoons position because the two bodies fit so closely together – like the bowl of one spoon sitting in another. It's a lovely cuddly position: the man lies behind the woman and pushes into her from behind. It can be a bit of a challenge to keep the penis inside, especially if it is shortish or one of you is carrying a bit of weight (because then your belly or your behind may get in the way). However, many women can feel exactly when the man is about to slip out, and, if this happens, they can push their buttocks towards their partner or change the angle of their pelvis slightly. If he still slips out, she can guide the penis in again. In this position, it's sometimes difficult – especially if it's dark or under the covers – to find the right opening, however experienced he is. On the other hand it's easy for him to play with her breasts or her clitoris. And if he leans his upper body back a bit, he will be at a very good angle to thrust really deep inside her.

69

This position is for oral sex. Why is it called 69? Think about the numerals. They look a bit like two people lying facing each other, both on their sides, but head to toe, so that their heads are opposite each other's sex organs. She has her head near his penis and he has his face near her vulva. Both partners can kiss and lick to their hearts' content.

People either love or loathe this position. Some people find it hard to give pleasure to someone else and enjoy themselves at the same time. It's not easy to know what to concentrate on. For others this is paradise on earth. Try it out and decide for yourself.

School of Love The Kama Sutra, a 2000-year-old Hindu text written in India, is the most widely read and famous source of practical advice on sex of all time ('kama' means sensual or sexual pleasure). The best-known translation into English was first printed (privately) in 1883. Dismissed by many as a scandalous work of pornography, the Kama Sutra is actually a handbook containing advice about all aspects of love including virtuous living and family life. It covers everything from how to choose a partner through dating to oral sex and provides detailed descriptions of sexual intercourse, as well as recipes for aphrodisiacs and advice to women as to how they should behave in disputes with their partners. So it's a comprehensive work. But it is most famous for its illustrations of numerous sex positions, which have been re-published many times: The Grip, The Eagle, The Glowing Juniper, The Goat, The Plough, The Crouching Tiger, and so on.

Missionary Position

Missionary Position (other way up)

Spoons

A few of the hundreds of positions in sex manuals, some more challenging than others. None are obligatory. Take your pick!

Viennese Oyster

Kneel and Sit

The Frog

Double Decker

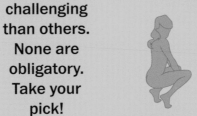

Reverse Cowgirl

The Star

Doggy Style

Doggy Style (low level)

Cowgirl or Rider

Missionary Position

Missionary Position
(other way up)

Spoons

Viennese Oyster

Kneel and Sit

The Frog

Double Decker

Reverse Cowgirl

The Star

Doggy Style

Doggy Style (low level)

Cowgirl or Rider

Anything else?

Of course, there are lots of other positions, but they are all, broadly speaking, variations on the ones that we've already described. See what you can come up with yourselves.

The important thing, no matter what position you select, is to make sure that you take deep, regular breaths and try to be as relaxed as possible. Keep to flowing, wave-like movements and try to alternate between tensing different muscles. Remember that slow and steady is often more exciting than frenzied thrusting in and out.

A good way to approach all of this is to think about the cat – an animal whose movements are lithe and supple. Suppleness is a great asset in sex. Bend your back while pushing your pelvis forward, then move in the opposite direction to give yourself a hollow back: your upper body will move at the same time. As the pelvis moves forward, the shoulders automatically follow so that they're rounded, like a camel's hump. When you reverse the movement, they pull backwards again. When your pelvis thrusts forward, your head drops almost of its own accord towards the nape of the neck, and then straightens up again. If all of this is a bit hard to follow, try getting down on all fours and watch what happens to your pelvis, shoulders and head when you cough. When you laugh hard or cough, your body makes pretty much the same movements we are describing. Or lie on your back, make a thrusting movement with your pelvis and watch what happens to your upper body and head. Try this when you're having sex and you'll notice the difference. You will feel much more if your body is moving rather than still. Excitement will course through your whole body, right down to your little toes.

Skill makes love unending.
Ovid

If, as suggested, you try moving with the slinky suppleness of a cat, your body will open itself up to even more feeling. You can savour your own sexual excitement to the full, while feeling and enjoying your partner still more. And the orgasm at the end of it will be mind-blowing. A wonderful, all-encompassing tremor will flow through the whole of your upper body and your pelvic area. That's the kind of soaring orgasm that takes you to another place – the one we're all after!

If this all seems a bit technical, don't worry. The more often you do it, the sooner it will become second nature. And you'll share and experience far more with your partner.

Sound Foundations – Good Vibrations The pelvic floor muscles are equally important for men and women. Many men don't even know they have a pelvic floor, and most don't realise that they can exercise it just as women do. The pelvic floor muscles contract automatically when we move. They also swing into action when we push or lift something heavy, or when we sneeze, cough or laugh.

The pelvic floor has several layers. The layer lying towards the back forms the floor of the abdominal cavity and supports the organs in the pelvis, thereby helping in the retention of urine, wind and stools. The layer lying further forward plays an essential role in a man's erection. And the pelvic floor also plays an important part in sexual satisfaction for both men and women.

Let's investigate where it is. Imagine that, when you are urinating, you try to interrupt the flow, or think about how it feels when you are trying to stop yourself from breaking wind. Certain muscles will automatically contract. Concentrate on that feeling, and you'll have found the pelvic floor.

Now you can practise tensing and relaxing it deliberately, and then try doing this during sex: women can use it to massage their vaginas from the inside. For men, a well-exercised pelvic floor is the foundation for a lasting erection.

Change of Scene

Now it's worth considering trying out not just new positions, but new locations. You don't always have to have sex in bed or at home.

Sex can happen anywhere: in the woods, on the beach, in the office, in the washroom at the restaurant, in a lift, while you're flying (strictly speaking illegal unless you are on a private plane), in a changing room. Or, if you want to know what is was like in the 1950s, in the car at a drive-in cinema. In those days, young people were not supposed to have sex before marriage, so they either hid away to sleep together or met for secret trysts. It's from those days that the story of keeping a needle in your trouser pocket comes, when people believed in the *penis captivus* phenomenon. During intercourse, it was said, the muscles of the vagina are capable of clamping down on a penis so hard that the man is unable to withdraw – as sometimes happens with dogs. Here's the kind of scenario they had in mind: two lovebirds are lying on a park bench making out under a full moon. Someone walks past, and the woman's alarmed reaction causes her vagina to constrict. Her lover is stuck fast, with no possibility of escape. What can they do? Luckily, he has brought a needle with him. He sticks it in his sweetheart's behind, and the shock makes her vagina let go. Out he slips, pulls his trousers up and *au revoir*! The idea of the clamping vagina is, of course, nonsense. Just as well that nowadays we know better.

BLOWJOB

She looked into my eyes and smiled. Then she crouched down until her head was lying between my legs. She started kissing my dick. I got hard immediately. Then she took it into her mouth. The feeling was beyond words: I thought I was going to pass out.

Fellatio. One of you gives, the other receives . . . and luxuriates, not just in the fantastic sensations that can be produced by mouth, tongue and hands, but also in the roles you're both playing. Watching as the other person focuses utterly and exclusively on giving you pleasure can be very exciting in itself.

> **Play Safe!** For oral sex, always use a condom – just as you would for intercourse – as this kind of contact also poses a risk of infection.

Oral sex is a gift to your partner, and it will only be enjoyable if it's provided in that spirit. If you're not sure whether, as the giver, you'll enjoy yourself, you could try starting that way and then move on to another position. Don't feel obliged to give a full blowjob straight-away: feel your way with this. When you're in bed with your lover, you could start by just giving tender little kisses in the area around the penis, for example. Gently take his scrotum in your hand, lick it until it's wet and then very lightly squeeze it or pull it. That will probably make him really hot, because he knows what's coming next. Now take his penis gently into your hand and play with it, squeezing it gently. While you're doing this, plant little kisses on the glans. If you don't know your partner very well yet, ask him to tell you how he likes to be held. That way you'll get the best possible instructions.

When you're giving a blowjob, hold the penis as though it were an ice-cream cornet or a lollipop. Lick it slowly and appreciatively along the whole length of the shaft, right to the top of the penis. Let your tongue circle – sometimes lightly, sometimes more firmly – over the glans. Use some of your saliva for lubrication – just enough to make it slippery. You can also gently suck the penis. Move your tongue against the glans as if you're saying 'lalala'. And if any of this makes you hot, let out a little moan – hearing how excited you are will turn him on even more. If licking doesn't do much for you, you can position yourself so that you are pressing your clitoris against his leg, which will allow you to satisfy yourself at the same time.

While you have his dick in your mouth, grasp it with one or both hands. You can continue with your hand the same rhythm you have

When I get down on my knees it is not to pray.
Madonna

Well, it's not my favourite thing on the menu, but you know, I'll order it from time to time, and, with the right guy, it can be nice.
Carrie, in Sex & the City

155

created with your mouth, one echoing the other. This should mean that your lips get less tired, because they aren't having to apply all the pressure. How hard you grip the penis in your mouth or with your hands depends on what your partner prefers. Some men like a bit less pressure, others prefer a little more. If you prefer not to take the penis too far in, you can make a little tunnel with your hands in front of your lips and let the penis slip through that first. Your partner can also take part, by gently rocking his pelvis while you are giving him head. You can control how deeply he pushes into your mouth by holding one of your hands against his belly.

It's worth remembering that the glans of a circumcised penis is often less sensitive than an uncircumcised one and needs a bit more friction. With an uncircumcised penis, if it isn't yet completely hard, you can suck gently on the foreskin. A limp penis is as sensitive as an erect one. Once it has got harder, push the foreskin carefully back from the glans, but take care not to push it too far as that can be painful. Some guys really like being close to the edge between pleasure and pain, and if that's true for your partner, you can both get some enjoyment out of it.

Favourite points for stimulation are: the ridged band of skin at the edge of the foreskin (the prepuce), the long underside of the shaft of the penis, and the seam in the skin that extends towards the anus. You can pay lavish attention to these with your fingers, lips and tongue. Try to pick up on how your partner is reacting to what you're doing: some people will want a firmer touch, others are more sensitive and need gentler handling.

Although you must be careful not to bite him as his penis is slipping in and out of your mouth, it can be really exciting for him if your teeth come into play. Sometimes it's easier for this to happen when the penis is not moving. Then you can have a delicate nibble, or even – if he says it's OK – gently bite him. As you can see, this is a case of getting feedback from your partner that tells you what works for him.

Giving a blowjob does not mean having his penis in your mouth all the time, or heaving it in and out as they do in porn movies. A guy who isn't particularly experienced would come far too quickly if you did this. In any case, unless you've done a lot of training, your jaw muscles simply wouldn't be able to cope. If your mouth gets tired, just carry on with your hands. That will allow you to gaze at his face and react to his expressions. Some men come straight away, others need more lengthy, continuous stimulation. At this point, it's better if you can avoid interrupting the rhythm.

When he comes, it's sometimes hard to know exactly when you should stop. Agree on some kind of signal that your friend can give you, or, just before he comes, get him to place his hands over yours. Then you can finish it off together and you can watch and follow

Easy?! You men have no idea what we're dealing with. Teeth placement and jaw stress, and suction and gag reflex. And all the while bobbing up and down, moaning and trying to breathe through our noses. Easy? Honey, they don't call it a job for nothing.
Samantha, in Sex & the City

what he does. After a while, knowing when to ease off will become second nature.

If you keep his penis in your mouth until he climaxes, there are various ways of dealing with his ejaculate. If he's wearing a condom, that will obviously collect the semen. If he isn't, you can either catch the ejaculate in your mouth and swallow it, or if you don't like doing that, just spit it into a handkerchief or whatever you have to hand. The taste of cum varies enormously – from sweet to really sour – and depends a lot on what a man has been eating.

What can be really exciting for both partners is if you take his penis out of your mouth at the last moment and press it against or between your breasts. Then he can come all over you. Lots of people really enjoy feeling the warm, creamy consistency of semen on their skin. But what about the face? You might already have seen a porn movie in which the man sprays the woman in the face. In real life, many women are not keen on this: if you get semen in your eyes, it makes them burn and it sticks your hair and eyelashes together. Some women, on the other hand, don't mind at all.

With all of this stuff, remember: just because you can, doesn't mean you have to. How you deal with semen is a matter of taste (!) and what kind of mood you're in. If you can't stand having semen in your mouth, be open about that with your partner or you'll have a horrible time. Lots of women dislike this, even though the porn industry would have you believe that you couldn't wish for anything more wonderful. If it doesn't appeal to you, make sure that your friend avoids ejaculating into your mouth, and then you can both enjoy the blowjob.

> **Blowing what?** Fellatio, blowjob, sucking off, giving head – there are lots of names for oral sex with a male recipient. Fellatio comes from the Latin word *fellare*, meaning to suck, which is pretty much to the point. So where did the expression blowjob come from? Maybe from the fact that a woman with her mouth full of penis has rounded cheeks, as though she is blowing? Another explanation is that in more prudish times people referred to oral sex as a 'below job', which gradually became known as a blowjob.

CUNNILINGUS

My head was between her legs. Her scent was driving me wild and her fanny looked like a swollen shell. I wanted to drive her out of her mind with my licking.

Licking needs time. Women like to know that they're in for a good journey rather than a quick trip – that way, they can relax more. The trick is to focus on what you are doing and to enjoy it. Imagine that you have a soft ice-cream that's beginning to melt: you need to keep licking it all the way around so that nothing gets lost. Think about it: in this position, your girlfriend is opening up the most intimate part of her body to you. It's not the same for a guy – your sex organs hang outside your body. A woman who lies open before you like this is particularly sensitive and may feel very vulnerable. So now you need to make her feel safe with you. Every woman is different in what she wants, so every vulva represents a new adventure. But here are a few orienteering tips:

Labia
The outer labia or lips are the least sensitive part, so, if your partner likes this, you can safely give them a gentle bite. The inner labia vary a lot from woman to woman: some are small, some are large, some are very fleshy, some less so. And they range in colour from pale pink to quite dark. The place where the outer and inner labia meet in the middle at the top is very sensitive, and as it can be the source of a lot of pleasure, it's definitely worth exploring.

Clitoral Hood
The clitoral hood is a woman's foreskin. It sits high up in the vulva near the clitoris and varies a lot in size, thickness and how tight it is.

Clitorial Glans
Found at the top of the vulva, the clitoris is more or less covered by the clitoral hood, depending on the individual. It gets larger when aroused. Remember: it's like a tiny penis.

Urethra
This is a small opening that is quite difficult to spot, located between the clitoris and the vaginal opening. Try to work out where it is. This is an important pleasure point and the opening through which a woman ejaculates, just like a man (for more on this, see page 202).

Vaginal Opening
This is low down between the labia. The most sensitive parts are directly around the opening and the first few centimetres inside. Further in, the vagina can only be aroused by pressure. You can't reach this part with your tongue, but you can with your fingers.

Prostate (G-zone)
This is inside the vagina. To find it, slide two fingers into the vagina with the palm of your hand facing upwards. When your fingers are almost completely inside, bend them upwards a bit and press carefully towards the abdominal floor (see page 202).

Other sites of interest

Her inner thighs and the skin close to the entrance to the vagina are also erogenous zones to be included in your exploration. The length of the vulva and the exact location of the clitoris can vary a lot. While you're licking, you'll be aware, at the nape of your neck, of these differences, because the angle you have to hold your head at will vary from partner to partner. Have a go. And when you go down on her, try using your whole face (your lips, chin and cheeks). You can also move your head up and down, from side to side or in circles. Ideally, your movements should be gentle and regular. Be careful if you have stubble on your face – it can be exciting, but it can also scratch.

The closer a woman gets to orgasm, the more firm and regular she will want the movements to be. But be careful not to overstimulate her, as that will spoil her pleasure and make it harder for her to come.

A word of advice for women: you might want just to lie back and enjoy, but perhaps you could try rocking your pelvis to and fro or make circular movements with it. If you are even slightly active, you'll become more aroused than if your body is completely passive and relaxed. You'll also be able to make sure that you get your clitoris into an optimal position. Expecting your partner to know exactly where to apply pressure with no help from you is asking a lot.

It's a good idea to think of the female blowjob as being divided into several phases. Most women do not race from nought to 60 in a few seconds, they need a bit longer.

During the first phase, it's worth getting an overview of her anatomy. While you're looking, start stroking her. Gently explore her vulva with your fingers, start giving it tender kisses, and the odd lick – slowly, carefully, feeling your way. Now start licking a bit more, using your tongue and your lips to work over the whole of her vulva. Alternate between making your tongue sometimes pointed, sometimes broad, and lick as though you're eating soft ice cream. Tense and relax your tongue so that it's sometimes soft, sometimes hard. And don't just use the top of your tongue, you can stroke and lick with its sides and underside as well. That will make for a really varied experience for you and for her. Play around with different speeds of licking and different pressures.

Be careful not just to follow your own agenda in all of this. You need to try to sense how your partner is feeling and react to her responses. Every woman reacts differently. Adjust what you do according to what she likes best. Now and then you might press your tongue, without moving it, gently against her clitoris, or take her inner labia softly into your mouth and suck on them. Without going directly to it, make more and more approaches towards the clitoris.

At this stage you can afford to be a bit more repetitive. Now you should be concentrating with your mouth on her vulva, moving your mouth and lips, with your mouth more or less open, letting your lower lip glide up and down, licking with your tongue, but always maintaining contact and never taking your mouth away. You could let one hand slide up to her breasts or stroke her belly, and then massage her just above the pubic bone. If you feel like it and you sense she does too, allow your fingers to feel gently inside her vagina. This may make her start wanting to have your penis inside her. Look at her every now and then, letting her know how much you love licking her. And close your eyes so that you feel even more. How long it takes to get to this point depends on lots of things. Sometimes it happens faster, sometimes it takes longer.

By this point, she'll be quite close to climaxing. Now you're licking her clitoris: stay with it, first very gently, then more firmly. Your tongue may be a bit tired by now, but all you need do is change the position of your head a bit. Or move your lower jaw, and your tongue will follow automatically, without it being too much of a strain for you. You might also, by this time, find yourself with your head in a position where you can hardly breathe! If so, change your position a bit so that your head is slightly tipped back. Find a position that allows you to keep licking her clitoris. Some women start groaning a lot and/or moving around at this stage, others do neither. A woman may just retreat into herself, and then you won't get any feedback because she's miles away, entirely wrapped up in what is happening to her. Have faith that what you are doing is hitting the mark. Or gently inquire whether everything is OK. Or you can ask her, for example, to lay her hands on your head to let you know when she is close to coming. When you've both done this a few times, you'll be able to tell what's happening from her movements and the noises she makes. You'll even know what it means when she's still.

From time to time you can draw back the little foreskin, or clitoral hood, so that your tongue can fully encompass her clitoris, but be careful not to use too much pressure. Or you could again insert a couple of fingers into her vagina. At this point, a lot of women yearn for the sensation of being filled. Sooner or later she's likely to climax and have an orgasm. Or maybe several, one after the other.

Here are some styles of licking that you might like to try:

Rattlesnake

This involves making small movements backwards and forwards with the tensed tip of the tongue – right, left, right, left. Use both the upper and the lower sides of the tongue. As the tongue dries off rather fast, you'll need to keep moistening it in the lower, front part of the mouth where saliva collects, just behind your bottom teeth. This is good for direct stimulation of the clitoris, but don't do it for too long.

O

Use both the upper and lower sides of your tongue to trace 'O' shapes directly on and around the clitoris – sometimes in one direction, sometimes in the other. This is a gentler movement than the rattlesnake.

8

Trace a figure of eight with your tongue. Again, you can use both the upper and lower sides of your tongue. The two circles that make up an eight can be quite small – draw freely. But aim to get the middle of the eight exactly on the clitoris.

V

Let your tongue slide down one side of the clitoris, over it, and then up the other side so you end up level with where you started.

I

Making your tongue as broad as you can, lick with one long stroke from below the clitoris to just above it and then down again. Use the top of your tongue on the way up, and the underside on the way down.

This oral caressing won't always end in earth-shattering orgasm, especially when you are not very experienced, or if you're not feeling very sure of yourself. Perhaps your partner can't yet give herself up completely to what you're doing. It will help if you tell her how much you love licking her, that doing this makes you really hot. If she hasn't ever had a climax, she may not do so when you're together, however good your technique is. It might be better for her to practise coming on her own before you try again to achieve this together.

A blowjob doesn't have to be about bringing someone to orgasm. It can just be a wonderful part of a bigger picture that involves building someone's excitement. If she wants to, she could make herself come while sitting on top of you, or in any number of other ways . . .

If she's having her period, you can still have oral sex (assuming, of course, that you have both had an HIV test). But not everyone is into this. If she's wearing a tampon, it can be almost business as usual, except that her orgasm is likely to be slightly different, because the vaginal area will be so well supplied with blood around this time.

ANAL SEX

Shrouded in secrecy, regarded as perverse and taboo – that's how anal sex was until recently regarded by most people in Europe and North America. Nowadays, it is far less likely to be considered an indecent or 'unnatural' practice. This has a lot to do with people realising that anal sex is not just for gay men, and that it can be enjoyed by heterosexual couples too.

Anal sex demands great sensitivity and a bit of patience. Anyone willing to explore it properly is likely to discover a highly intimate and very intense aspect of sex.

If you feel like having a go at this, you might want to explore your own anus to start with. Apply some lubricating cream or gel, or saliva, or moisture from the vagina, and use your own or your partner's finger to gently investigate the entrance of your anus. If you want to, you can insert a finger – and that will start to give you an idea of how it feels to be entered from behind. Some people find that caressing or entering the anus with a finger or two brings so much pleasure that it is as far as they want to go. How much further you want to take this, and whether you want to follow up with full-scale penetration is for each person to decide independently.

If you do want a penis to enter you, it often helps if it is lubricated, so that it slips in as easily as possible. You need good control to practise anal sex: take things step by step and make your movements slow and careful. Begin by massaging the anus with your fingers, and then gently insert one or two fingers into it. This can be very exciting, and it opens up the muscles a bit. Your partner can help by giving instructions like 'Stop!' or 'Go on!' or 'More!' It makes everything simpler if the receiving partner is fully relaxed, and of course the more aroused he or she is, the easier it will be.

Some people think that anal sex is unhygienic. It needn't be. The crucial thing is that a penis should never be inserted into the vagina after it has been inside the anus unless it has been thoroughly washed, or the condom changed, in between. This is because bacteria that live in the bowel can cause infections in the vagina.

Some people think that it is essential to have colonic irrigation (i.e. to wash out the bowel) before you have anal sex. Others think that this is completely unnecessary. What is important is that you feel good about it, so if you can relax completely only if you know that you are as clean as possible, taking a shower or bath together can make for some very nice foreplay.

It's not just a male partner who can do the penetrating: lesbian couples use strap-on dildos, and even a woman in a heterosexual relationship can have a lot of fun indulging her man anally. The person using a penis or a dildo to penetrate someone else is usually described as the active or giving partner, and the one being penetrated is the passive or receiving partner. How two partners experience their respective roles is very different. Men penetrating the anus of a female partner tend to find it a particularly exciting because the anus is narrower and more muscular than the vagina. But the person in the receiving role, whether male or female, can also get a lot of pleasure from anal sex, and even be brought to orgasm by it. Many women have reported having their best orgasms while being penetrated anally and at the same time having their clitoris stimulated. But that takes a bit of practice.

> **Black Hole** Please do not stick objects up your anus. The muscles that make up your sphincter are extremely strong and can produce a prodigious sucking action. Objects removed by doctors in accident and emergency departments have included: a vibrator (accompanied by the salad tongs used for a failed removal at home), a live artillery shell, a bottle of body spray, a cell phone, a pint glass, a toy car, a handgun, a potato and a glass light bulb. Removing foreign objects from the anus is no fun for anyone involved. If you really want to push something into your anus, use anal plugs that are designed for the purpose and so are broader at the base than at the end that is inserted – making them very unlikely to be sucked in.

THRUSTING TECHNIQUES

Having a penis pushed rapidly in and out of the vagina and always at the same angle, as in porn movies, does not do a lot for a woman. So we're going to tell you about two techniques that should be more fun.

Not many people realise that the cells inside the vagina are different from those around its entrance. Near the outside of the body, the vagina reacts very well to rubbing, whereas further in, pressure works far better. It's more interesting for the man, too, if he doesn't just confine himself to thrusting in and out. If he moves his penis around in various directions while penetrating the woman, he, too, will feel more.

Imagine a sparrow and a whale. The tiny sparrow moves in rapid, short bursts. The whale, on the other hand, is a rather ponderous creature that makes slow, deep, unhurried movements. It's worth alternating between these two styles of movement in sex. When he is thrusting into his partner, a man can be first a sparrow, then a whale. The sparrow thrust is small and delicate, rather like a bird pecking up crumbs. Tap, tap, tap. In terms of sexual intercourse, that means that the man is not penetrating very far into the woman – he's getting maybe five to six centimetres inside her and almost out again. Inspired by the movements of the whale, however, he will find himself far deeper in her vagina.

Try using this pattern of thrusts (no laughing!)

first 9 x sparrow, then 1 x whale
then 8 x sparrow and 2 x whale
then 7 x sparrow and 3 x whale, and so on

As you can see, the number of sparrow thrusts goes down by one each time, and the number of whale thrusts goes up by one. It's dead simple, but can be intriguing and exciting for both partners. If you get that far, carry on until you've got down to 1 x sparrow thrust followed by 9 x whale . . .

You can also try the sparrow/whale combination of movements when giving head to a male partner, especially if you're aiming for him to climax. The sparrow action would involve wrapping your lips around only the head of the penis. The whale action would mean allowing the penis deeper into your mouth. Use the combination of movements described above or make up your own. See how long he can hold back from ejaculating. One more thing: a sparrow/whale blowjob works well in the rider or the frog position, with the woman sitting on top.

The Mortar Bomb works like this: the man slips his penis into the woman. He pushes in so that he's quite deep but instead of then pulling out as usual, ready to push in again, he stays where he is. He thrusts a bit from this position, staying deep inside almost all the time. He could, for example, do five or seven deep thrusts while inside, before he withdraws and does two normal thrusts from outside her body to deep inside again. And then stay inside for a while again.

For the Screwdriver, just as the guy is thrusting in deep, he makes circles with his hips. It's easier to do this in a standing position or from behind than when lying on a bed. This rotating movement is crucial for the Screwdriver. Practice makes perfect.

The move called the Earthquake is for advanced candidates. The man places both hands on the woman's hips, penetrates her and shakes, as best he can, both his own and her pelvis. Then everything starts vibrating like a jackhammer. The Earthquake technique is the one that needs the most practice, because he needs to have a very flexible pelvis and well-trained pelvic floor muscles for it to work.

ALL IN THE MIND

Unfamiliar men and women, unusual locations – the start of an exciting fantasy. Of course we get excited at the sight or scent of our partners, but another common and important element in sex is fantasy. If you've already devised your own sexy little daydream: congratulations! That may well provide you with the final ingredient that catapults you to climax. Sometimes, though, you can feel bad that your partner is playing little or no part in your thoughts as you come. Or maybe you're worried that your fantasies are becoming

Some people are better imagined in one's bed than found there in the morning.
P.J. O'Rourke

164

increasingly extreme. Many people find that what they imagine is not at all what they would actually do or experience: some people even fantasise about being forced to have sex. A survey published in the 1970s by the famous American research team, Masters and Johnson, revealed that in the USA at that time forced sexual contact was the first or second most common sexual fantasy whether a person was homosexual or heterosexual, male or female. Which of course does not mean that those same people wanted to experience this in real life.

Indulging in sex fantasies just before orgasm can give the ultimate kick to the experience. But you don't have to reveal what you're thinking about. Few people expect ever to act out these kinds of fantasy in reality, though you may be able to incorporate some part of them into your lovemaking. If, for example, you fantasise about being held down forcibly and being given orders, tell your partner about this and find out if he or she is willing to play this out. Maybe you imagine having sex in a threesome or a foursome? Your partner might have been having the same fantasies as you. If so, talking about them could lead to some hot sex.

Fancy a Quickie? You don't always have to have lengthy and elaborate sex for it to be good. It depends on how you feel at the time. It's a bit like deciding what you want to eat. Sometimes a burger can seem like the most delicious thing in the world, while at other times all you want is some good home-cooking. On another occasion you would be happy to sit down to an elaborate three-course meal. Like fast food, instant sex is spontaneous, shortlived and happens with little preparation or fuss. Day-to-day sex takes more time, but is on the whole not very ambitious. Gourmet sex usually involves careful planning and preparation and can result in hours and hours in bed.

Now we've given you a few tips and suggestions, maybe it's becoming clear that when it goes well, sex can be like a fantastic series of dances, full of joy and sensuality: endless kissing, gazing into each other's eyes, caressing, exploring, trying out different positions . . .

It can be a lot more enjoyable if you go on kissing and cuddling all the way through rather than doing it only at the very beginning. Often, as soon as the penis is in, everything else is forgotten, and there are no more tender little caresses and embraces until much later. That just leaves thrusting, keeping it up and coming. But you can pause and interrupt the race to orgasm. Lots of people find sex even more enjoyable if, as they build to a climax, they go on exploring each other's bodies, kissing, touching, stroking . . .

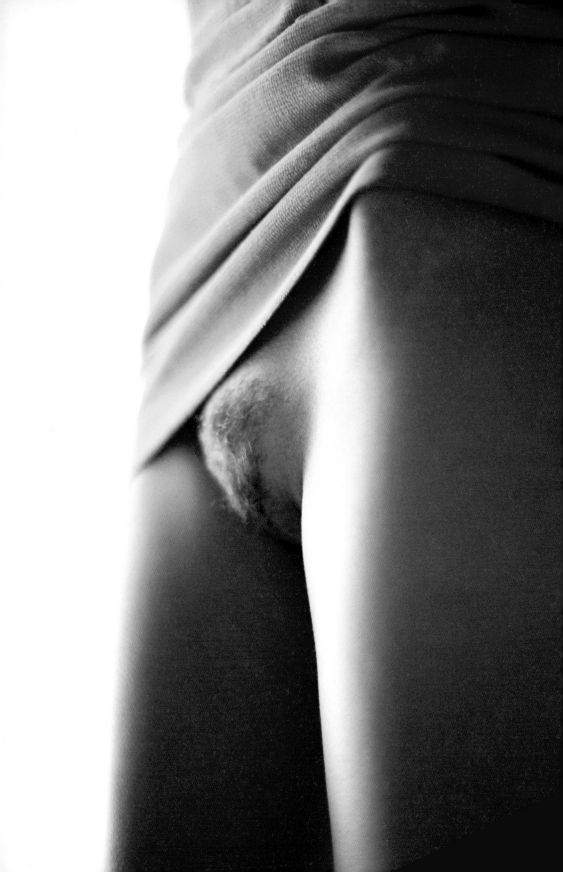

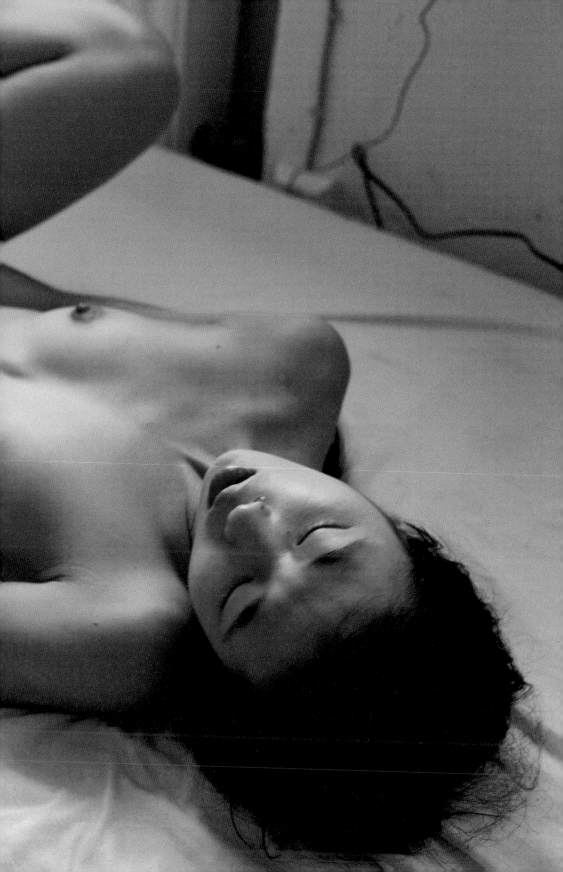

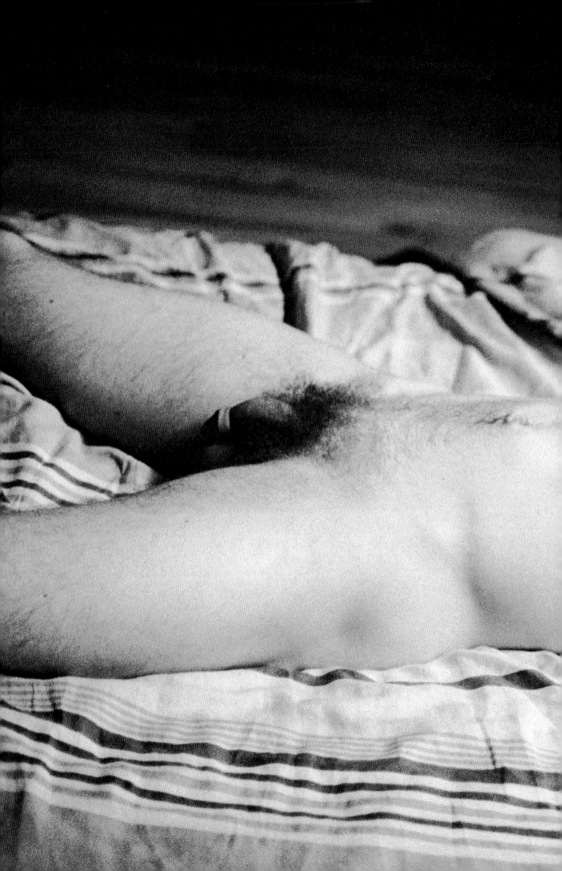

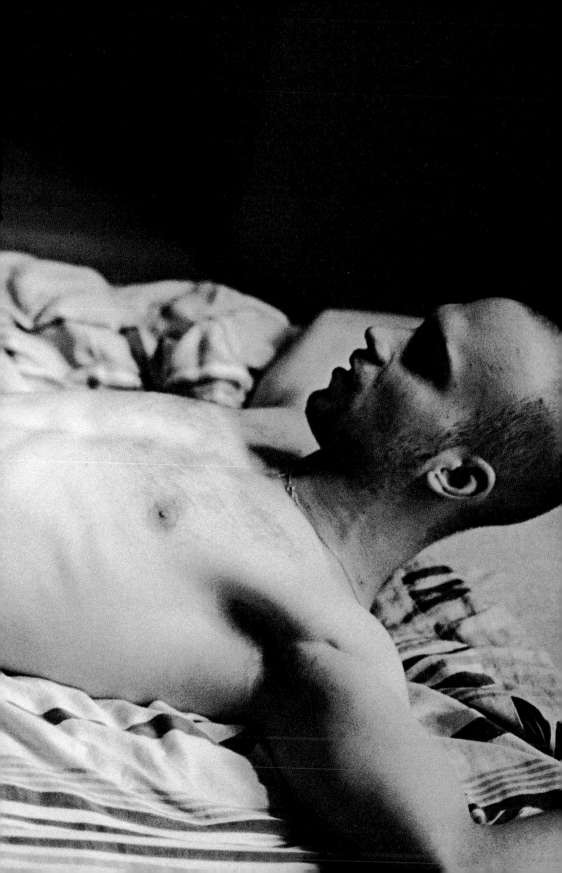

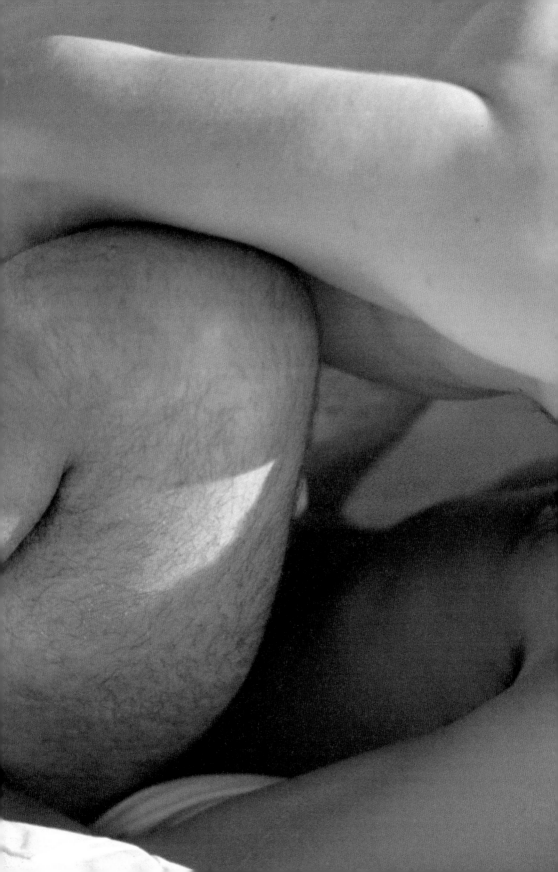

I'M COMING!

THE ORGASM

BLISS

There's a tingling, a throbbing and your heart is racing. You feel a convulsive jerk, an explosion, and then – a massive sense of relief. If orgasms didn't exist, we would definitely not have as much sex and would therefore reproduce less. So orgasms guarantee the future of the human species. Nature has organised things very cunningly: having an orgasm is a reflex, so anyone is capable of having one – though getting there can be a bit tricky. Practice makes perfect.

Flying Solo

Knowing how to have an orgasm is all about what you have already taught your body to do, what patterns of reactions your nerve cells have been learning right from the first time you masturbated. Exactly what you do when you masturbate has a big effect on how easy and enjoyable you'll find it to have sex with someone else later on. Remember those information pathways we talked about that are being laid down in your brain continuously as you learn and practise new techniques?

In my next life I want to live backwards. Start out dead and finish off as an orgasm.
Woody Allen

There are different sorts of nerve cells. Some respond to pressure, some to stroking or other slow movements, others to pain. If, when you masturbate, you tend to do so by using pressure, that is the kind of sensation pathway that will rapidly become established. The idea of trying out new ways of getting there doesn't even occur to you. Why bother deviating from your original route, when you know you can reliably reach orgasm in record time? That's all fine, but once you have a partner, you may find that what you've been doing on your own doesn't work quite as well as you might have hoped when there are two of you.

Everyone's way of reaching orgasm is different, and some methods for getting there can be quite surprising. Most people rub or put pressure on their sexual organs in one way or another, tensing their bodies as they do so. Like this, for example:

Electric flesh arrows . . . traversing the body. A rainbow of colour strikes the eyelids. A foam of music falls over the ears. It is the gong of the orgasm.
Anaïs Nin

A girl lies on her front in bed, her legs crossed. She pulls her shoulders up and back, flexing her whole body while she presses her fist against her clitoris. She, too, scarcely moves her pelvis. It may take a bit of effort to bring herself to orgasm. And there may be more satisfaction in the sensation of relief after coming than in the climax itself.

A boy sits in front of his computer, leaning back slightly, with his feet pressing into the floor, tensing his torso and arms while he holds his penis, moving his hand rapidly up and down. His pelvis doesn't move at all. His orgasm is fast and enjoyable, but it doesn't last long and is centred on his genital area.

A girl rubs her clitoris with her fingers, using small, rapid movements and concentrating on one tiny area. Her orgasm, when it arrives, is a popping sensation, shortlived and limited to her sexual organs.

A young man lies completely relaxed on a bed and jerks off, which he does by holding just the glans of his penis between two fingers and gently stroking up and down. He keeps this going for ages. At some point his whole body tenses, he increases the pressure on his penis and he comes.

Those are four examples of perfectly good masturbation techniques. But sex involving two people is often rather different. Look over the examples above again, and imagine in each case what would happen if a partner joined in. Usually it will mean a lot more moving around. Your partner may touch you differently from how you have got used to touching yourself – more firmly perhaps, or not hard enough – and you may find that you're tensing muscles more or less than you do when you're alone, simply because you'll be lying or sitting differently. Or, if you're a guy, the vagina feels wetter and doesn't grip as tightly as your hand. Small differences like these can mean that sex doesn't go quite as you expect it to. Suddenly a boy finds himself coming too soon, or a girl can't come at all. Now it's more important than ever to know exactly how your own patterns of arousal work.

We've already mentioned that boys tend to have an easier time of it as far as getting excited is concerned. For most boys it happens almost automatically. Even so, few people of either gender know much about their own sexuality. Most boys will find themselves touching their penis more and more often, but they still have to learn how particular sensations can be created, and how to direct or control them. Most girls have even more to learn, as they will know little or nothing about their vulvas and vaginas. So we'll start by providing a few tips for girls about how to train for orgasm.

ORGASM TRAINING FOR GIRLS

Make your bed really cosy and comfortable. Lie down on your back with your knees up and start slowly stroking yourself all over. After a while slip your fingers gently down to touch your labia – using a bit of body oil (preferably unperfumed) can be really nice – and then start gently pressing or massaging your vulva and clitoris. You can touch your clitoris, without drawing back its foreskin, by stroking across it from left to right and back again. If you work your fingers up and down, the foreskin is likely to move up and down too, exposing the clitoris completely. Some women find this painful, and if you do, just stick with stroking from side to side. You could also slip a finger into your vagina and begin gently exploring it. Gradually, your body will start to become aroused of its own accord. Many women, at least to begin with, find stimulating the clitoris is the easiest way to get to orgasm.

As your excitement grows, it helps if your fingers concentrate on the clitoris and move with a fairly regular rhythm, perhaps pressing a little more. You might also want to speed up the movements a bit. If you then move your pelvis backwards and forwards or in circles, the feelings of pleasure and excitement will spread further, and your whole body will become more and more excited. If you feel like ratcheting up the experience even more, keep moving your pelvis, while you continue to touch yourself and take deep breaths. When you feel yourself inching towards a climax, concentrate more on alternating between tensing your body and relaxing, simply by using more powerful movements. For some people, this will provoke an orgasm, and for others it will take longer. This pleasuring can last five minutes or it can last an hour. It's how you get there that counts.

> **The Final Stretch** If you feel as though you are cresting, but you just can't come, a few deep breaths and some good thrusts of the hips can give you the extra oomph that you need. Or you can let out a few deep moans. That will activate your pelvic floor, which will often trigger orgasm. You should, of course, be actively using your pelvic floor already. Make it contract and relax as though you are operating a kind of internal pump. Note that antihistamine tablets or sprays used to treat hay fever and other allergies are among the medications that can create problems with achieving orgasm. The reason for this is that the body needs histamines in order to climax. The good news is that as soon as you stop taking the medication, everything will go back to normal.

Although it's often a while before girls get to know much about their vulva and vagina, they still have a big advantage over boys in one respect: a girl won't be caught off-guard by becoming suddenly and visibly aroused in the way that a boy can be. Sometimes, not having that reflex can seem a pity, but girls are spared the often deeply embarrassing experience of being caught out by an unexpected stiffy at the swimming pool, say, or on the sports field. On the other hand a lot of what happens to girls is very similar to what happens to boys, when desire strikes and lust takes over.

Your pulse races, your blood pressure rises. The skin on your neck and breasts is flushed. The nipples become hard and the breasts get bigger – up to 25% larger than their usual size. Both the inner and outer labia become fuller and darker, as a result of the increased blood supply to them. The clitoris also swells with blood, and stiffens, just like a penis. The vagina becomes moist. These changes are more discreet than those that happen to a man, which is why some women are hardly aware of them and may be unsure of themselves or anxious: *Am I aroused enough yet?* But you can rest easy in the knowledge that your body will do everything it can to allow the penis to slip into you as easily as possible: the uterus moves a little higher and pulls the vagina up and back, an effect sometimes referred to as 'tenting'. For some women, this produces an urgent desire that they describe as wanting to be 'filled' – a sensation that is actually a reflex.

Researchers often see sexual desire as dividing into several stages:

Arousal

Touching erogenous zones and/or having erotic fantasies produces a state of arousal. The labia and the clitoris swell, the outer labia begin to part and the vagina becomes moist. The breasts become somewhat larger and more sensitive to touch. The nipples harden and become erect. Breathing and heart rate speed up.

Plateau

The entire genital area swells as more blood flows into it, and all your senses concentrate almost exclusively on this area. Breathing gets even faster, muscular tension increases. Blood pressure and the rate of breathing continue to rise. The clitoris becomes erect, though this sometimes goes unnoticed if it is still concealed beneath its foreskin.

Orgasm

An orgasm begins with muscular contractions of the vagina, the uterus and the sphincter and can last up to 30 seconds, or sometimes even longer. Exactly how this feels is different for each woman.

Returning to Normal

Muscles relax and within half an hour swelling has subsided. The clitoris, vagina and uterus all revert to their original positions. By contrast with men, who need a bit of time to recover, some women can go on having one orgasm after another (although this is often easier to achieve on your own than with a partner.) After the first orgasm, a woman will slip back into the plateau stage and then build up to another climax.

That was a rather technical description of orgasm. But of course emotions, as well as anatomy, play a crucial part and we'll talk about that aspect a bit later.

NERVOUS ENERGY

Both the pudendal nerve and the pelvic nerve are fantastic at producing orgasms. The pudendal nerve lights up the vulva and the front third of the pelvic floor. An orgasm originating here tends to be limited to the genital area. The pelvic nerve is more tied up with mood and emotion. Physically, it affects the urethra, the female prostate (G-zone), the bladder and the rest of the pelvic floor.

Whether these two nerves are responsible for different kinds of orgasm, and how these differ, has been the subject of much discussion. But it is actually very difficult to define what kind of orgasm you have just had. Even when it is only a woman's vagina that is being directly stimulated, there is probably some indirect clitoral stimulation happening at the same time. So there's not much point in trying to differentiate between orgasms. The key thing to remember is that movement makes all the difference. If you're allowing yourself to move around a bit, you'll have better blood circulation, which in turn enhances sexual pleasure. And the reverse is true too: if you lie stiff as a board in bed and hold your breath, you will feel less.

As we've already mentioned, some women are multi-orgasmic. That means that they are able to have one orgasm after another, and, unlike men, don't need even a short pause after coming. But a lot of women report that after a clitoral orgasm, the clitoris is so sensitised that it would be uncomfortable to continue. On the other hand, with a mainly vaginal orgasm involving the prostate, a woman is likely to feel quite relaxed about going on. And then there are orgasms that are so awesome, no matter what kind they are, that there is no need or desire to pursue another one.

Since the time of the earliest humans, the brain stem has been the driver for our most basic instincts prompting us to run away from danger, to fight, to find food, and to seek out sexual partners, and some orgasms originate here. But it is also possible to have an orgasm set off by the parts of the brain that are responsible for fantasies, imagination and consciousness. Sexual desire, erotic enjoyment and orgasm can all be triggered by these much less instinctive parts of the mind. This opens up a whole world of possibility. Once we have figured out how to use these capabilities to the full, we might even be able to learn how to think ourselves to orgasm! Many people are already unconsciously making use of these abilities when they turn to particular fantasies to help them come. Unfortunately it can work the other way round as well: our consciousness, or certain thoughts, can stop an orgasm in its tracks. If you don't like yourself or you dislike your own body, for example, or there is something you can't allow yourself for some reason, your mind will be elsewhere, and you'll be tense and ill at ease. In that state of mind, trying to have an orgasm is like trying to scale Everest.

He slides himself inside her, her heart is bursting. The pithy organic organ can't hold all that she feels for this man. When she reaches her peak, her brain supernovas, a small, perfect death.
Mrs Alenko

201

EROGENOUS ZONES

We've already mentioned the female prostate (the G-zone). If you insert two fingers into your vagina, with your hand facing palm upwards, you can feel it close to the abdominal wall. Imagine you're inserting a tampon, but position your fingers so that they can reach up inside. Alternatively, you can squat and bear down gently, as you would when peeing, and use a mirror. In this position, part of the wrinkled surface of the prostate is visible in many women. When you first touch your prostate, it may feel numb or even uncomfortable. Most women find this changes over time, and that it's worth persevering – think of it as gradually stroking your prostate awake.

Here's an idea of how to do this:

Lie down on a bed and relax. Insert two fingers into your vagina. Start massaging your G-zone by tracing small circles slowly and firmly. Let all tension flow out of your body, which will also mean extending your pelvic floor. You do this by pushing it out – it's a bit like the muscular movement you make just before urinating, but don't worry, when you are sexually excited, the entrance to the bladder automatically closes. Have you ever tried to urinate just after having sex? Usually you have to concentrate really hard to make it happen. So relax, keep pushing down a little, resist the temptation to pull up again, and massage this erogenous zone. Savour the sensation and let your excitement build.

When the prostate is stimulated, fluid builds up in it which will later flow from the urethra as ejaculate. If you massage or stroke your prostate on a regular basis, you'll find that you will be able to feel more during normal sexual intercourse as well.

FEMALE EJACULATION

We've mentioned above that small quantities of fluid from the prostate – generally between one and five millilitres (up to a teaspoonful) at most – can trickle out through the urethra during sex. But some women find themselves producing spurts of far more liquid, which can be a bit surprising. This is a mixture of fluid from the prostate and very dilute urine that has been catapulted out of the bladder and through the urethra. Usually, there's somewhere between three and 50 millilitres of liquid, but it can be a lot more if large quantities of water have been drunk just beforehand – which is what female porn actors sometimes do for maximum effect.

THE MALE ORGASM

Before we talk about the male orgasm, we'd like to explain a few things about erections and the five stages of arousal.

Two things are crucial to erections: blood supply and pelvic floor muscles. Erectile tissue runs along the entire length of the penis. When a man is aroused, this tissue fills with blood and makes the penis hard. Neurotransmitters in the brain are, among other things, responsible for this increased supply of blood. They are what give the command for an erection to happen. Strangely enough, this begins with an instruction to relax. A penis is wrapped in a thin layer of muscle, and, when there is no erection, this prevents more blood from flowing into it – otherwise men would have permanent hard-ons. If an electrode were to be introduced into a limp penis to monitor activity, you would hear a barrage of sounds as the nerve cells kept up sustained salvos of impulses to prevent the erectile tissue from filling with blood. When a man becomes sexually aroused, the in-struction goes out to these muscles to *let go!* Simultaneously, the arteries widen to speed up the delivery of more blood, which starts to happen immediately. Increased pressure causes valves in the veins that normally take blood away to close, and the pressure builds still further. The penis becomes hard and rises up. Pelvic floor muscles help to support the penis and provide the back-up needed to sustain an erection.

Male arousal can be divided into five phases. And this is not just to do with the penis: the whole body is involved.

The problem is, God gave man a brain and a penis and only enough blood to run one at a time.
Robin Williams

Blood circulation
Most of the time, a penis is limp, the body relaxed and breathing is even. At the start of an erection, the arteries widen and blood flows into every fibre of the penis. Breathing becomes deeper, valves in the veins close. The tip of the penis turns darker.

Swelling
Blood supply to the penis increases, and it begins to lift itself up. The head of the penis turns reddish-blue, becomes a bit rounder and, with the help of muscles in the pelvic floor, raises itself up from the testicles. Muscular tension increases all over the body and the nipples become hard and sensitive. Pulse and breathing rates speed up.

Stiffening
The erection is now well underway. The penis is full of blood, and it becomes darker still. It is now fully erect, and the foreskin (assuming it is still intact) is by now usually drawn back. Pulse rate and blood pressure

rise, breathing becomes faster, the testicles fill out, tighten and draw closer to the rest of the body. Sometimes a few drops of moisture may trickle out of the penis, perhaps already containing sperm.

Climax

The penis has now reached its maximum size, which can be as much as double its normal length and girth. Blood pressure climbs still further, as does the breathing rate. Ejaculation happens at the moment of greatest tension. Suddenly it feels as though everything is contracting and then exploding at the same time. That is the moment when semen spurts out.

Subsiding

The penis becomes limp again, and as this happens the muscles mentioned at the beginning once again prevent any new supply of blood reaching the erectile tissue. Your breathing slows down, and your body relaxes – until next time.

One more issue of interest to most men: how can a guy recognise – before it's too late – when he is approaching his 'point of no return', in other words, the moment when he can no longer hold back from climaxing? A bit of background information is needed here: there's the loading stage (emission) and the firing stage (ejaculation).

EMISSION

The first stage, emission, is a reflex, and the conscious part of the brain is not involved. Just ahead of ejaculation, three different fluids collect in a small chamber that forms the rear part of the urethra just in front of the bladder. So far almost no liquid has left the penis. Both the external and the internal sphincters (circles of muscle) of the bladder are closed to stop urine escaping and the space between them is where the semen collects.

The three fluids that make up semen are:

> 1: fluid from the prostate – thin and watery
> 2: seminal fluid (containing sperm) that has been stored in the epididymis
> 3: liquid from the seminal vesicles – thick and creamy

Sperm, which are produced in the testicles and stored temporarily in the epididymis, account for only 5% to 10% of semen. Ejaculation follows soon after emission. But beware: part of the ejaculate is released well before orgasm and this trickle of fluid will occasionally contain sperm. That is why withdrawing the penis from the vagina just before the man comes is definitely *not* a safe method of contraception.

EJACULATION

Semen spurts out through the urethra shortly after emission. Everything is controlled from a nerve centre in the spinal cord, which is activated when the semen has collected, during emission, in a space called the bulbous urethra. The pelvic muscles expel the semen under high pressure in a series of three to seven contractions, each lasting less than a second. Sometimes there will be only a small amount of semen, at other times more.

High-protein shake Between the ages of 15 and 60, a man will produce an average of 30 to 50 litres of ejaculate, containing 350 to 500 billion sperm.

So, as you can see, various different holding chambers and liquids are involved. It's perhaps not surprising that if there is a variation in certain muscular contractions, the ejaculate is diverted so that instead of shooting out forwards through the penis, it is channelled backwards into the bladder. If that happens, next time you pee the urine will look slightly milky. This is perfectly normal.

Knowing what stage of arousal you have reached is useful because it gives you more control. You'll know when you need to hold off a little if you want to avoid coming just yet. Gradually you will become more aware of slight physical changes that signal what stage you have got to.

It's good for a girl to be able to interpret these signals as well, so that she knows how far along her partner is. An important stage to be able to recognise is the one just before emission. And the sign that this point has been reached is not the slight pulling sensation that many guys feel just before coming, but the moment when the glans is at its most sensitive. By the time you feel the pulling sensation, it's already too late – the semen is on its way.

It is possible to delay a climax by relaxing your pelvic floor, but it takes a bit of practice. Get yourself aroused until you're almost at the point of no return and concentrate on how you feel at that moment. Then try tensing and relaxing your pelvic muscles while you use slower strokes and breathe deeply. Don't stop stimulating yourself altogether. Do the same exercise three to five times, before you come. In time you'll get a better and better idea of exactly which stage of arousal you've reached.

BLUE BALLS

Is there such a thing as blue balls? Yes. Does getting an erection mean that a guy has to ejaculate? No – nothing bad is happening to a guy's body if he has an erection and doesn't come. Those blue balls are not damaged, and nothing is going to explode. Sometimes, if you're in a state of arousal for a long time, and your testicles remain swollen with blood, they can develop a bluish tinge as a result of blood in the scrotum gradually losing oxygen. This causes no damage, though the build-up of pressure can be uncomfortable – anything from a mild ache in those supersensitive balls to feeling as though you've been kicked in the crotch. If you don't ejaculate, your erection will just subside of its own accord. Having said that, it is healthy to ejaculate. There is some research to show that men who ejaculate a lot as teenagers actually live longer! They tend to suffer fewer heart attacks, strokes or prostate cancer. Anyone who masturbates several times in one day will discover that they produce diminishing amounts of ejaculate, sometimes only a few drops. And after that much activity, it will take about three days before the much-quoted teaspoonful is produced again. That's all entirely normal. And another thing: the longer foreplay lasts, the more nerve activity there will be in the relevant parts of the body and the greater the quantity of semen produced. That's why there tends to be more ejaculate as a result of sexual intercourse than when a guy masturbates alone.

TAKE CARE!

CONTRACEPTION
& SEXUAL HEALTH

PROTECTION

Protection is about two things: not getting pregnant and protecting yourselves from sexually transmitted infections (STIs). There is a whole range of ways to avoid pregnancy, but there is only one good method to use against infections, and that is the condom.

There are pros and cons to every form of contraception. Make sure you find about all the alternatives before you decide which one is right for you. For most methods, it is girls who have to take action, but it is just as important that boys find out about this too. You may want to talk to one or both of your parents about this or to do the research online or both. Contraception services are free and confidential in the UK for everyone including young people under 16 years old. This means that the doctor or nurse won't talk about you to your parents, or anyone else, so long as they believe you are mature enough to understand the information and decisions involved. Most general practices provide advice and prescriptions, otherwise you can go to a contraception clinic, sexual health clinic or a young people's service. Involving a parent in your decision is encouraged, but if you do not want to tell your parents what you are doing, you have no obligation to do so. If a partner is not going with you to see the doctor or health advisor, take a good friend so that you can talk over the issues with someone. Which form of contraception is most suitable for you will depend on lots of factors, like whether you want a method that you have to use (and think about) every time you have sex, every day, or much less often. In the UK, you need a prescription for all contraceptives except condoms and, if you meet the criteria, emergency contraception (available at a pharmacy – see page 215).

No glove, no love.
Lauren Oliver, Before I Fall

Contraception should be used on every conceivable occasion.
Spike Milligan, Puckoon

The **Pearl Index** is the most widely used data (involving clinical trials) for judging the effectiveness of different methods of birth control. It estimates how many women out of a 100 will become pregnant in a year using specific methods of contraception. The lower the method scores on the Pearl Index, the more reliable it is. Regular sexual intercourse without any form of contraception produces the following results in the first year: 85 pregnancies in 20-year-olds, 50 pregnancies in 30-year-olds, 30 pregnancies in 40-year-olds. Between 45 to 50 years old, when, for most women, the menopause kicks in, the number drops to zero.

HORMONAL METHODS

Hormonal contraception is one of the safest methods, because, as long as the hormones are taken into the body without a break, they work all the time. But beware – this also means that contraceptive pills are effective only if taken continuously.

The progestogen-only pill (or mini-pill), contraceptive implant, contraceptive injection and intrauterine system or IUS all work by giving the body doses of progestogen, which thins the lining of the uterus (making it impossible for a fertilised egg to attach to it) and thickens cervical mucus (preventing sperm from reaching the egg). With the injection and implant, ovulation stops. The mini-pill prevents ovulation in some cycles.

There are two types of contraceptive pill – the **combined pill** and the **progestogen-only pill** (or **mini-pill**) – and many varieties of each. The combined pill usually makes periods regular, lighter and less painful. On the mini-pill, periods may stop, be irregular, light or more frequent. No matter which pill is being taken, its effectiveness may be reduced if a woman vomits or has diarrhoea, or if she forgets to take it. If any of these things happen, a condom should be used. The combined pill won't be prescribed if you have a family history of deep vein thrombosis, if you smoke or have migraine headaches or if you are very overweight. The mini-pill may be suitable for women who can't take the combined pill. Fewer than one woman in 100 using contraceptive pills will get pregnant in a year.

The **contraceptive patch** (a patch stuck on the skin) and the **contraceptive vaginal ring** (a small plastic ring inserted into the vagina) make periods more regular, lighter and less painful for many women. A new patch is used every week for three weeks out of four, and the vaginal ring is also used for three weeks out of four. Neither is affected by other medicines, diarrhoea or vomiting. Neither will be prescribed to women who are very overweight. Fewer than one woman in 100 will get pregnant in a year using either of these methods.

The **contraceptive or hormonal implant** is a small flexible rod that is inserted under the skin of the upper arm under local anaesthetic. It works for three years but can be taken out sooner. Periods may stop, be irregular or last longer. Not affected by diarrhoea or vomiting, though some medicines may stop it working. Fewer than one woman in 1000 will get pregnant over three years.

The **contraceptive injection** lasts for twelve weeks (Depo-Provera) or eight weeks (Noristerat). Periods may stop, be irregular or last

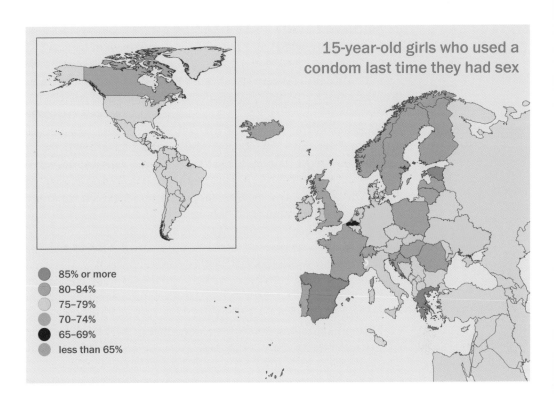

15-year-old girls who used a condom last time they had sex

85% or more
80–84%
75–79%
70–74%
65–69%
less than 65%

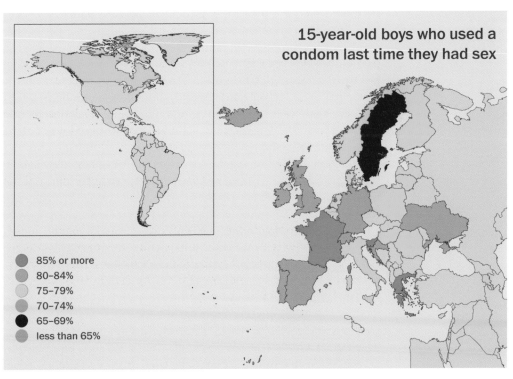

15-year-old boys who used a condom last time they had sex

85% or more
80–84%
75–79%
70–74%
65–69%
less than 65%

longer. Not affected by other medicines, diarrhoea or vomiting. Fewer than four women in 1000 will get pregnant over two years.

The **intrauterine system (IUS)**, sometimes known as the **Mirena** (a brand name), is a small T-shaped plastic device that is put into the uterus. It works for five years but can be taken out sooner. Irregular bleeding or spotting is common in the first six months, and periods may stop altogether. Not affected by other medicines, diarrhoea or vomiting. Fewer than one woman in 100 will get pregnant over five years.

Many women use hormonal contraception without experiencing any adverse side effects, but there is a range of physical effects and/or mood changes that can occur. With so many alternative methods, you may need to try more than one before you find what is right for you, or opt for a non-hormonal, barrier method instead.

BARRIER METHODS

Condoms, diaphragms and the female condom all work by preventing sperm from reaching the ova (egg cells).

Condoms, also known as sheaths, rubbers, raincoats, French letters, johnnies, among many other names, score 2 to 18 on the Pearl Index. It's important that a condom is new, undamaged and applied properly. Jewellery, long fingernails or even the sharp corners of the packet can all tear or puncture this super-thin membrane, so it needs to be carefully unwrapped and handled. Condoms kept for weeks in a wallet or a warm trouser pocket may start to perish.

> A condom is the glass slipper of our generation. You slip one on when you meet a stranger. You dance all night, and then you throw it away. The condom, I mean, not the stranger.
> *Maria Singer, in Fight Club*

Condoms are the only contraceptive device that simultaneously protects against both pregnancy and infections. They are widely available in pharmacies and supermarkets, and many bars and clubs have condom dispensers in their washrooms.

Applying a condom can be turned into part of foreplay. Seeing the funny side of this rather awkward ritual is fine. You can kiss the penis, examine it at close quarters together, and stroke it a little, and then slip the condom on. Both girls and boys should learn how to apply a condom. Boys can try this out when they're masturbating. Girls can practise with a partner, but if they really want to plan ahead, they can have a go at putting a condom on a banana.

Here's how to use a condom:

The condom must be put on before intercourse starts. If you put it on inside out by mistake, start again with a new one. Don't turn it the right way around and use it again: there may already be sperm or bacteria on it.

Pull the foreskin back. Flatten the end of the condom between two fingers and press the air out to make room for the semen that it will catch. The ring of the condom must be in direct contact with the glans. Then, keeping it as smooth as possible, unroll the condom down the length of the penis.

After ejaculation, keep hold of the condom on the shaft of the penis as you pull out of the vagina. When the penis has started to shrink again, take the condom off, being careful to leave the semen inside. Give it a quick check to make sure that there are no holes or rips in it by gripping the end of the condom between your fingers and squeezing: no air or fluid should escape.

Avoid using oil-based lubricating creams or gels or massage oils as these may react with and damage the latex from which most condoms are made. If you do discover that a condom has ripped or slipped off after ejaculation, and you definitely do not want to become pregnant, don't just hope for the best. Get hold of emergency contraception as soon as possible (see page 215).

Having sex using a condom takes a bit of getting used to, but it does mean that you can stop worrying about picking up infections or the risk of pregnancy and get on with enjoying yourself.

Condoms are the oldest form of contraception. In days gone by they were made from fabric or sheep intestine. The earliest versions covered only the glans. 'Lambskin' condoms are still available and are considered by aficionados to provide the most pleasure of any type of condom because they are so thin and transmit body heat better than latex. They work well as a contraceptive, but do not give adequate protection against STIs. Most condoms are now made of latex and come in a range of sizes, colours, surface textures and even flavours. Because they are so elastic, the average size fits most guys. Be honest when you're buying them: if it's too big it will slip off.

The **diaphragm** or **cap** is a dome-shaped, spring-rimmed cup made of silicone or latex that is put into the vagina to cover the cervix before sexual intercourse, so preventing sperm from entering the uterus. The diaphragm is available in different sizes and must be fitted by a health professional and used with spermicidal jelly or cream. The cap can be inserted up to two hours before sexual intercourse or just before you have sex. It has to stay put for at least six hours after intercourse, and if you have sex more than once during that time, you'll need more spermicidal cream or gel. Used correctly, with spermicide, the diaphragm is one of the most reliable contraceptive methods, but its rating plummets if it isn't inserted properly, so the rate of pregnancy in a year is between four and eight women in 100.

> **Not Spermicidal Enough!** Never rely on spermicidal (meaning 'sperm-killing') products alone. Their effect lasts for only an hour, and no cream or jelly can act as an effective barrier to sperm reaching an egg.

Female Condom

In Sri Lanka, where until recently no-one had heard of the female condom, female sex workers in Colombo marketed it as a sex toy, charging more when they allowed the client to insert it – a real thrill, as seeing a vagina up close, or touching one, is a huge taboo in Sri Lanka. In Senegal, the condoms are sold with noisy 'bine bine beads', an erotic accessory worn round women's hips: the rustle of the polyeurathane during sex is now associated with the clicking of the beads. and so, a turn-on. Senegalese women also cleverly suggested that the capacious female condom reflects the size of their partner's penis. And in Zimbabwe, a new word 'kaytec-yenza' has appeared – to describe the pleasurable tickle created by the inner ring rubbing against the penis. *From an article in The Guardian, August 2005*

Often referred to by the brand name Femidom, the female condom is a thin, soft, loose-fitting pre-lubricated polyurethane sheath that lines the vagina and is 17 to 18 cm long. A ring at the inner, closed end is used to insert the condom, in a similar way to inserting a diaphragm. The ring at the outer end remains outside the vagina. This is the only method a woman can use to protect herself from sexually transmitted infections if her partner refuses to use a condom. Handling the female condom takes a bit of practice, and it can make weird rustling noises during sex. Five women in 100 will get pregnant in a year.

Intrauterine Device (IUD) or coil

This is a small plastic and coiled copper device that stops sperm reaching an egg and is also a chemical contraceptive because the copper ions in the spiral are toxic to sperm. Once fitted it can stay in position for five to ten years depending on the type. Good for women who want an internal barrier method and who react badly to hormonal contraception. Periods may be heavier or longer and more painful. Not affected by other medicines, vomiting or diarrhoea. Less than two women in 100 will get pregnant over five years.

NATURAL METHODS

Some people practice contraception by guessing where the woman is in her monthly cycle, and assume that if women are fertile only around ovulation – which happens on the fourteenth day or thereabouts – it is safe to have unprotected sex the rest of the time. Relying on this kind of rough calculation is like playing Russian roulette. Young women, especially, often have highly irregular cycles. As sperm can survive inside a woman for up to a week, you can almost never assume that you are completely safe. Also, occasionally, more than one egg may be produced in a month. Natural methods are really suited only to couples who are quite happy for a pregnancy to occur.

Coitus interruptus, or withdrawal, which means pulling the penis out before ejaculation, is a completely unreliable method, because even the first few drops of liquid that emerge when a man is aroused, and before he ejaculates, may contain sperm. An even bigger problem is that young men are simply not as good as they would like to be at knowing exactly when they're about to come. So don't even think about relying on withdrawal as a method of contraception.

The best natural methods rely on accurately identifying the fertile and infertile times of the menstrual cycle. There is a small, handheld computerised monitor (brandname Persona) with test sticks that measure hormonal changes in a woman's urine. If used correctly this method can be 94% effective. The disadvantages are that it's estimated to take three to six cycles to learn how to use the system effectively, you have to keep strict daily records and you must avoid sex or use a condom at fertile times of the cycle, whenever these may be.

STERILISATION

Sterilisation for a man involves less invasive surgery than female sterilisation. Both operations are extremely difficult to reverse – if not impossible – to reverse. Sterilisation is a permanent method of contraception suitable only for those who are sure they will never want children (or don't want any more). That's why doctors will not perform the operation on young men or women without being absolutely certain that it is appropriate. Counselling is important, especially if you are young: in ten or fifteen years' time you may feel differently.

Sterilisation for a man (vasectomy) involves cutting, sealing or tying the tubes that carry sperm from the testicles to the penis, under local anaesthetic. Men who have been sterilised and their female partners report little or no difference in their sex lives after the operation. Ejaculate is made up of three liquids, and two of them are still flowing – only the sperm are missing. About one in 2000 male sterilisations fail to stop sperm being produced. Sterilisation for women, which involves cutting, sealing or blocking the Fallopian tubes, is a bigger operation, usually carried out under general anaesthetic. Afterwards, a woman's periods are unaffected. About one in every 200 female sterilisations fails.

EMERGENCY CONTRACEPTION

It is crucial that you use contraception *before* you have sex. Emergency contraceptive pills (aka the morning-after pill) should be treated as just that and resorted to only when, for some reason, your chosen method of protection has failed. There are two types of drug: levonorgestrel (brand name: Levonelle) can be taken up to 72 hours after unprotected sex, and is available on prescription or, in the UK, over the counter in a pharmacy, and ulipristal acetate (brand name: ellaOne), which can be taken up to 120 hours after sex and is available only on prescription. Both of these morning-after pills work by

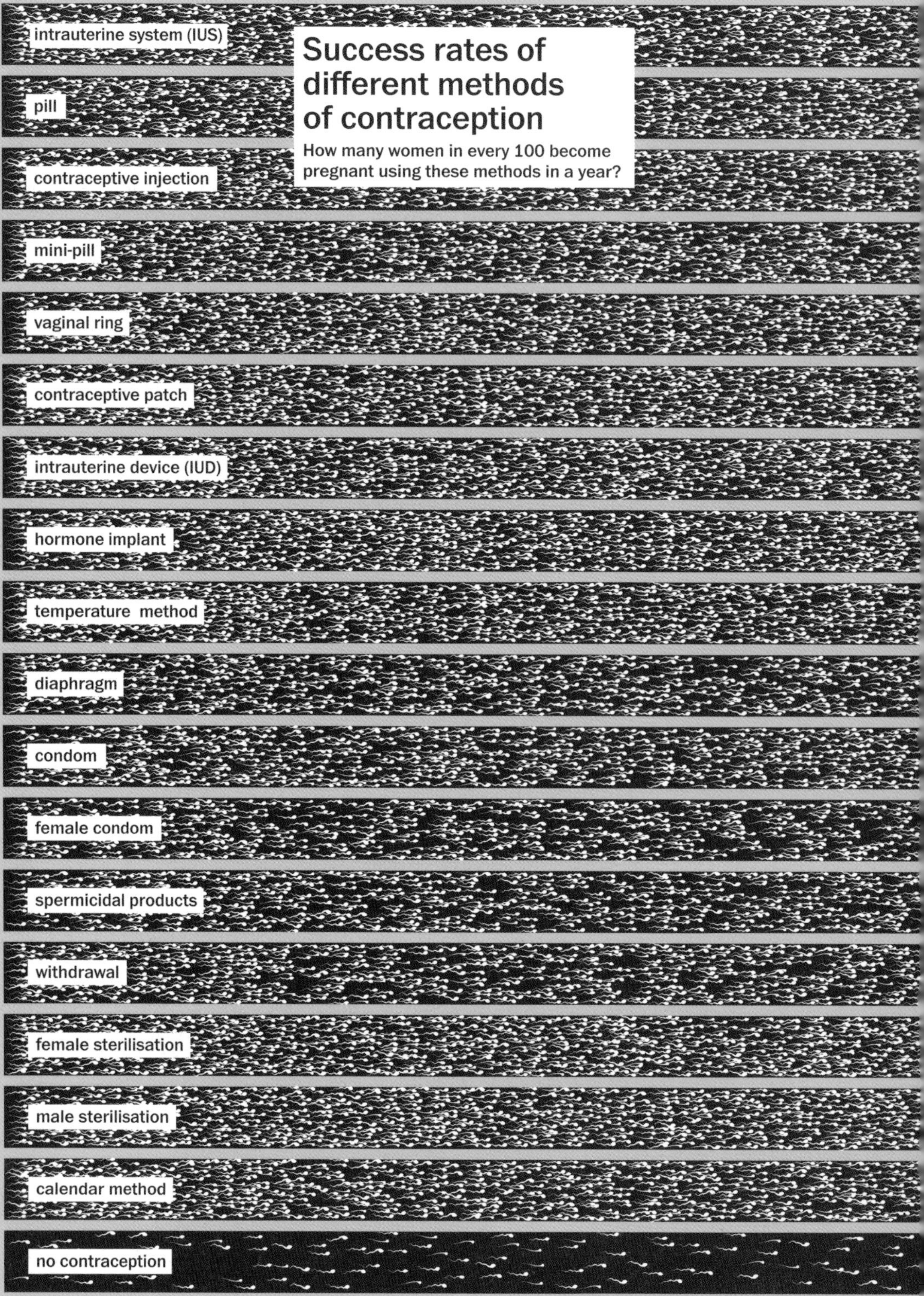

Success rates of different methods of contraception

How many women in every 100 become pregnant using these methods in a year?

intrauterine system (IUS)

pill

contraceptive injection

mini-pill

vaginal ring

contraceptive patch

intrauterine device (IUD)

hormone implant

temperature method

diaphragm

condom

female condom

spermicidal products

withdrawal

female sterilisation

male sterilisation

calendar method

no contraception

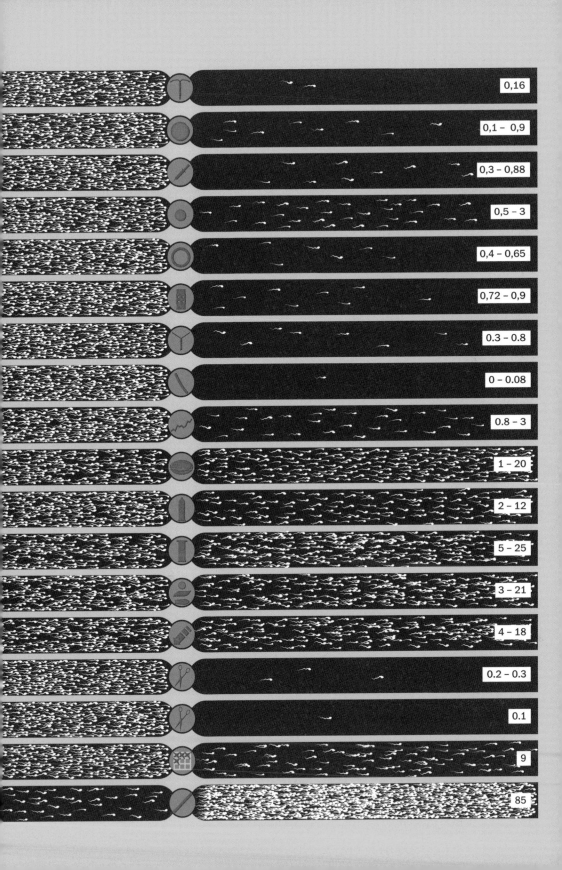

preventing ovulation, and, if an egg has already been produced, stop its development and prevent it from attaching to the lining of the uterus. Fitting a coil (IUD) is a highly effective form of emergency contraception, but it can be difficult to arrange for this to be done fast enough, i.e. within the recommended five days after sexual intercourse or the earliest possible date of ovulation. If you need emergency contraception, check with a health professional that any medication you are taking will not reduce its effectiveness or stop it working altogether. In a few individuals, the morning-after pill may cause nausea, vomiting, swollen and tender breasts, headaches, abdominal pain and spotting or breakthrough bleeding.

ACCIDENTAL PREGNANCY

It was not so long ago, even in the developed world, that for girls who got pregnant by mistake it was nothing short of a disaster – and that still remains the case today in many parts of the world. Faced with the dire consequences of their situation (such as being rejected by family, losing a partner, losing a job, being made homeless), many girls tried all sorts of (sometimes dangerous) methods of inducing an abortion, including taking very hot baths, doing punishingly vigorous exercise, jumping down steps or binding their abdomens. As none of these methods was effective, many women resorted to back-street abortionists who would attempt to remove the embryo from the womb using chemicals or instruments such as knitting needles – techniques that usually involved a lot of pain and blood and quite often led to the woman's death. Later, forward-looking doctors began to perform abortions for some of these desperate women, in spite of risking heavy penalties if discovered, including being struck off the medical register. In many countries and in some American states, it remains illegal to have or perform an abortion, and even in countries where the law allows the procedure, there are anti-abortion organisations that campaign vehemently, often on religious grounds, against termination of pregnancies. Equally, there are organisations convinced that it is a woman's right to choose whether or not to take a pregnancy forward.

Modern clinical practice in abortions means that for most women there are scarcely any physical after-effects. The damage is more likely to be emotional, sometimes becoming evident only years after the event. For most women, the decision to have an abortion is not straightforward and is certainly not taken lightly. For that reason alone, abortion should never be relied upon as a method of contraception. If you are struggling with issues surrounding pregnancy and/or termination, see page 250 for organisations that can help you.

WHAT HAPPENS WHEN A PREGNANCY ENDS?

It's estimated that up to 20% of pregnancies end of their own accord, resulting in miscarriages (also called spontaneous abortions), most of which happen during the first twelve weeks. Some happen so early that women don't even realise that they were pregnant and may simply experience particularly heavy bleeding. NB: if you suspect you might be pregnant (but have not checked), do not assume that bleeding necessarily means that a pregnancy is at an end.

Let's say that you have had sex and the guy came inside you. Maybe you were just careless and had unprotected sex, or perhaps the condom broke. No method of contraception is perfect. Now you're scared that you might be pregnant. What should you do? Assuming that you do not wish to continue a pregnancy, the first thing you should be thinking of is emergency contraception (see page 217), which is designed for exactly this kind of situation but must be used within five days of having unprotected sex. If it is later than this and you suspect that you might be pregnant and are worried about what to do, go to a doctor. The order of events is: pregnancy test, counselling to decide whether or not to continue with the pregnancy, pause of a few days (if possible) for the women to consider how she wants to proceed, then a decision about whether or not to terminate the pregnancy.

A termination (or induced abortion) can be very hard to handle emotionally. You may, for example, be very fond of the person with whom you have become pregnant, and/or have already started to have maternal feelings, in spite of all the difficulties that would be presented by having a baby. Maybe you have never felt completely convinced about the idea of having an abortion, or you're scared of the operation itself? Or perhaps your partner has not behaved or reacted to your news quite as you had hoped. What is important is that you act quickly. The earlier an abortion is performed, the lower the risk of complications. Try to discuss the matter with an older friend whom you trust, or talk to your parents or to a doctor. Having an abortion will not have any effect on your ability to get pregnant later or on future pregnancies. In the UK, girls under 16 judged to be capable of reaching an informed decision may opt for a termination.

TERMINATION OF PREGNANCY/ABORTION

If you decide to have termination, you will probably have a medical abortion – i.e. using drugs. These drugs, not to be confused with the ones used for emergency contraception, are used after the fertilised egg has lodged in the lining of the uterus, in other words, once a woman has tested positive for pregnancy. Often referred to as the abortion pill, there are actually two or three kinds of medication involved: first, an artificial steroid called mifepristone that blocks

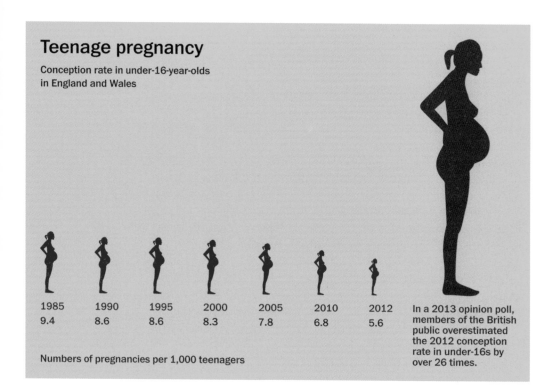

Teenage pregnancy

Conception rate in under-16-year-olds
in England and Wales

1985	1990	1995	2000	2005	2010	2012
9.4	8.6	8.6	8.3	7.8	6.8	5.6

Numbers of pregnancies per 1,000 teenagers

In a 2013 opinion poll, members of the British public overestimated the 2012 conception rate in under-16s by over 26 times.

progesterone (a hormone essential for pregnancy), and leads to the opening of the cervix, then two days later another tablet (prostaglandin) is taken, causing uterine contractions that expel the lining of the womb together with the gestational sac and the embryo. A further drug, misoprostol, can be used if necessary. What happens is similar to a miscarriage or a particularly heavy monthly bleed. The drugs are taken under medical supervision. It's a good idea to have a check-up two weeks later to make sure all is well.

SEXUALLY TRANSMITTED INFECTIONS (STIs)

STIs are infections passed from one person to another during sex. Some people can be quite casual about STIs, sometimes to the point of acting truly recklessly. Some think that if they get an infection, they'll just take a pill for it or use some cream, carry on as normal, and everything will be fine. They couldn't be more wrong. Chalmydia can cause infertility in women. Some STIs can lead to cancer (human papilloma virus, for example) or life-threatening infections (HIV, hepatitis). It's no good thinking that this cannot happen to you. At least one in four young people will contract an STI before they are

25. And as you can never tell who has one and who hasn't, there is one unbreakable rule when you have sex with a new partner or someone you don't know: USE A CONDOM. If you are in a trusting, settled relationship, and both of you have been checked out for STIs, then you can choose whether to use condoms or not. But of course if you don't use one, you still need to choose another form of contraception.

Anyone in a long-term relationship who has sex with another person without using a condom must do the decent thing and get tested for HIV before sleeping with his or her partner again. That will mean a significant pause in your sex life, as it takes three months to get the all-clear. One of the unfortunate things about STIs is that the symptoms often do not show up until after you have already had sex with your regular partner again, and – hey presto! – you've passed it on. So if you do have sex without a condom with someone other than your partner, get tested immediately. Remember that if you go to a health professional for advice and/or treatment of any sort, including STIs, confidentiality is a given. If you go to a GUM (Genito-Urinary Medicine) clinic, you will be screened for a range of STIs and the results will be back quite quickly. Make sure you take a break from sex until you know you are in the clear. In most cases your partner will need to be treated too, and it won't be possible to avoid having a conversation with him or her on the subject.

Often, once you have tested positive for an STI, previous partners, as well as your current partner, will need to be tested. As this can be very challenging for personal reasons, sexual health clinics have protocols for contacting previous partners without disclosing your details (contact tracing, often by phone text). In this way everyone who is at risk can be cared for.

STIs show up in a variety of ways with a range of symptoms.

CHLAMYDIA

One of the most common and widespread STIs, chlamydia is triggered by a bacterium and usually affects the cervix and the uterus in women and, in both sexes, the urethra, but it can also infect the anus, eyes, mouth and throat. The majority of cases are found among under 25-year-olds, but it can be caught by anyone. It is estimated that one in twelve sexually active 20-year-old women in the UK have chlamydia and one in fifteen sexually active 14- to 19-year-olds in the US. For many people, this is a so-called 'silent' infection as it is often symptomless, so it is easy to pass on unwittingly. Left untreated, chlamydia can lead to pelvic inflammatory disease (PID) and cause the Fallopian tubes to become blocked, leading to infertility. Most cases of PID occur in women aged 15 to 24.

Symptoms Research suggests that 50% of men and 70% to 80% of

HIV diagnoses in Europe
per 100,000 population

Western Europe
6.6

Central Europe
1.9

Eastern Europe
22

Transmission methods
as percentages

Heterosexual sex

35.3 24.6 60.2

Men having sex with men

41.7 26.2 1.2

Injecting drug use

5.1 7.3 33.6

15-to-24-year-olds

Proportion of total cases as a percentage

9.8 15.4 10.1

Male-to-female ratio

3 to 1 4 to 5 1 to 4

For lists of countries in each region, see page 254

women have no symptoms after being infected. However, symptoms can include a slight burning sensation when you urinate, unusual cloudy or white discharge from the penis, vagina or rectum, pain or discomfort at the end of the penis, abdominal pains (especially during sex), and, in women, bleeding between periods or after sex.

Treatment Chlamydia is easily treated with antibiotics, but it is important that this happens as early as possible and that both partners (as well as other sexual partners from the previous six months) are treated, whether or not they have symptoms.

GENITAL HERPES

Herpes simplex virus (HSV) causes painful sores and blisters and can affect any mucous membrane (moist lining), such as those found in the mouth (everyone has heard of cold sores), as well as the genitals. There are two strains of the virus. Most cold sores are caused by HSV-1, and most cases of genital herpes are caused by HSV-2.

By the age of 30, around half the population of the UK has been infected with genital herpes as a result of having unprotected sex (vaginal, anal or oral). Once you have contracted the virus, you will have it for life. HSV remains mainly dormant (inactive), but it can recur at any time – on average four to five times in the first two years after infection, and then less frequently, with each subsequent outbreak being less severe. Many people have only a single outbreak. Someone with HSV is infectious only during an outbreak, but the infection is highly contagious and easily passed on by skin-to-skin contact. HSV does not affect future general health or fertility.

A word of warning: cold sores can be infectious for eight days after the blisters have healed, so you should avoid kissing or oral sex until the end of that time, otherwise your partner could develop cold sores and/or genital herpes. HSV-2 cold sores can occasionally result from oral sex with someone who has genital herpes.

Symptoms At least eight out of ten people carrying the virus have no initial symptoms and so are unaware that they have been infected. The symptoms, when they arrive, are sores, blisters, pain and inflammation, especially on the genitals.

Treatment Antiviral treatments that prevent the virus from multiplying are available on prescription. The sooner you take the medication after an outbreak begins, the faster the sores will heal. Some people report a tingling sensation that allows them to anticipate an outbreak and catch it by taking antiviral medication early. To prevent the spread of genital herpes, it is important to avoid sex until symptoms have cleared up and to continue to use a condom afterwards. (NB: over-the-counter remedies for cold sores have no effect on genital herpes.)

Remember, what happens in Vegas stays in Vegas. Except for herpes. That shit'll come with you.
Sid Garner, in The Hangover

223

HUMAN PAPILLOMA VIRUS (HPV)/GENITAL WARTS

Different members of this family of viruses are responsible for warts on fingers, feet, hands, nails and head. Genital warts – one of the most common STIs – are the result of a viral skin infection caused by human papilloma virus (HPV). HPV is spread by skin-to-skin contact, so it is passed on through unprotected sex (vaginal and anal) and shared sex toys, but also through kissing and intimate caressing. It is most likely to be transmitted to others when warts are present, although it is still possible to pass the virus on before the warts have developed and after they have disappeared. Condoms provide good, but not complete, protection because it is possible for the skin in the genital area not covered by the condom to become infected.

Symptoms Warts appear around the genitals and the anus, and consist of small fleshy nodules that may grow larger to become cauliflower-like ulcers or cysts. They are usually benign growths, but some can precede cervical cancer and cancers of the penis and anus. It can take over a year for warts to develop, so, if you are in a relationship and discover that you have genital warts, do not assume that your partner has been unfaithful.

Treatment The best place for treatment of genital warts is a GUM clinic, where a full screening for STIs will be carried out. Genital warts are usually removed using cream, lotions or chemicals, but a doctor may recommend physically removing them with cryotherapy (freezing the warts using liquid nitrogen) or laser treatment. In the UK, a vaccine to protect against the strains of HPV known to cause 70% of cases of cervical cancer is available nationally to all teenage girls up to the age of eighteen; it also protects against almost all types of genital warts. HPV vaccines offer the best protection when all three vaccine doses are administered and the individual has time to develop an immune response before becoming sexually active with another person.

If you are diagnosed with genital warts, it's preferable to avoid having sex, including anal and oral sex, until your genital warts have fully healed – both so that you don't pass on the infection and to speed your own recovery.

GONORRHOEA

Sometimes referred to as 'the clap' or 'the drip', gonorrhoea is the second most common bacterial STI in the UK. Worldwide there are an estimated 60 million new cases each year. The infection is passed on through infected mucous membranes in the genitals, bladder, anus, mouth and the conjunctiva on the inner side of the eyelid. Gonorrhoea cannot be caught by casual contact (toilet seats, swimming pools, saunas).

Symptoms Its nickname, 'the drip', refers to the bad-smelling, yellowish-green or bloody discharge from the vagina or, in both sexes, from the urethra. Two to seven days after this first appears, the vagina or urethra will become inflamed. If untreated, the bacteria may spread and cause inflammation of the prostate, epididymis and ovaries. If the rectum is infected, there may be anal discomfort. Like chlamydia, gonorrhea can affect the whole abdominal cavity, and may result in potentially life-threatening infections as well as pelvic inflammatory disease (PID) which can cause infertility.

Treatment A swab is taken from the penis or cervix. If it proves positive, the infection is treated with antibiotics. It is essential that both partners are treated, otherwise they may go on passing the infection between them.

HIV/AIDS

AIDS is the illness that results from infection with the Human Immunodeficiency Virus. HIV can be passed on when infected blood, sperm or fluid from the vagina gets into another person's bloodstream. During sex, especially anal sex, mucous membranes often sustain some damage. The virus cannot penetrate healthy skin or membranes, but it can find its way in where there is even slight damage. HIV weakens the immune system, and once the body has been subjected to multiple illnesses, it becomes unable to protect itself and develops AIDS (Acquired Immune Deficiency Syndrome).

Although the risks of contracting HIV are lower with oral sex than with sexual intercourse (since the virus is not carried by saliva), it is still crucial to use a condom as any tiny lesion in the skin could allow the virus to be passed on. Anal sex is considerably more dangerous than vaginal intercourse simply because the skin inside the anus is damaged so easily.

Fortunately, the virus is relatively fragile. That means that in a normal environment, it dies quickly on contact with air. So no risk is posed by hugging, shaking hands, sharing drinking glasses, using the same toilets, and so on. Keep in mind, if you are planning to travel abroad, that HIV is more prevalent in some other countries than it is in the UK.

Symptoms It is often years before any symptoms develop and AIDS kicks in. Some people report a range of symptoms just after they have been infected, including fever, swollen lymph glands, sweating, tiredness, stomach problems or weight loss, though all of these could have other causes. Only an HIV test (a blood test carried out professionally) can give you a clear positive or negative. Anyone who has unprotected sex with multiple partners as a matter of course should make sure that they are tested regularly for HIV.

Treatment AIDS is incurable. However drugs are now available that mitigate its effects and extend the life expectancy of AIDS sufferers, although not without a range of side effects. These drugs have to be taken for the rest of the patient's life. Whether or not HIV and AIDS are notifiable conditions (meaning that cases have to be reported to a government agency) varies from country to country. In the UK, for example, neither is notifiable, while in Ireland and Australia both are, and in New Zealand, only AIDS is.

HEPATITIS B

Hepatitis (inflammation of the liver) can be triggered by a number of different viruses – you may have heard of Hepatitis A, B, C, D and E. Hepatitis B is the one most commonly passed on through sexual contact via bodily fluids (mainly blood, but also in vaginal secretions, ejaculate and saliva). You can also get infected through the use of non-sterile instruments in ear piercing, acupuncture or tattooing, needles in drug misuse, or by sharing razors or toothbrushes.

Symptoms Many people are unaware of their infection until they develop symptoms, between one and six months after contracting the virus. These can include nausea, vomiting, lack of appetite, flu-like symptoms such as tiredness, general aches and pains and headaches, and yellowing of the skin and eyes (jaundice). After about five weeks, the viral infection is usually over, but among otherwise healthy people infected as adults, around 6% to 7% will develop chronic hepatitis. People with chronic Hepatitis B can still pass the virus on to other people, even if they have no symptoms. A fifth of chronic sufferers will go on to develop scarring of the liver, which can take 20 years to develop, and around one in ten will develop liver cancer.

Treatment There is currently no specific treatment for acute Hepatitis B other than painkillers and bed rest. Chronic hepatitis is hard to treat, but a combination of antiviral drugs can be used to slow the spread of the disease and prevent damage to the liver. There is a vaccine which is thought to be 95% effective, but in the UK, where Hepatitis B is relatively rare, it is not provided as a matter of course.

SYPHILIS

Syphilis is caused by a bacterium (*Treponema pallidum*) and is passed on, when an ulcer is present, during unprotected sex, stroking and kissing. In much of the developed world, including North America, the UK, Australia and New Zealand, the majority of cases now occur among homosexual and bisexual men, and at present infection rates are rising steadily. In other (especially developing) countries, the disease is much more common in both sexes.

Symptoms One to twelve weeks after infection, a dark red mark or spot appears on a man's glans or foreskin or a woman's vulva, vagina or cervix, though it can be in the mouth or in the rectum as a result of oral or anal sex. After a few days, the spot becomes a flattened yellowish ulcer with a hard edge (usually painless), from which a clear, highly infectious fluid oozes. After a while, the ulcer heals up, but unfortunately its disappearance means not that the infection has gone, but that it has entered the bloodstream. From there, over the next few weeks, it will spread through the entire body. Symptoms are flu-like and typically include fever, pain in the joints, swollen lymph glands, and rashes on the hands and feet. The mucous membranes in the mouth become inflamed and often the tonsils as well. Hair begins to get thinner. After two or three months these symptoms may well have vanished completely, and with them the disease itself. But in some people, syphilis will recur, and in the worst cases there will be problems with balance and/or speech, dementia, amnesia or even death.

Treatment A swab can be taken from a sore and tested, or if the ulcer has gone, a blood test can detect syphilis. The earlier treatment begins (with an antiobiotic), the faster the recovery. Syphilis is a notifiable disease in the USA and Ireland (doctors must report cases to the authorities), but not in the UK, Australia or New Zealand.

TRICHOMONIASIS

The most common STI across the world, but fairly uncommon in the UK, Trichomoniasis is caused by a tiny parasite called *Trichomonas vaginalis* (TV) that can affect the vagina and urethra in women and the urethra and sometimes the prostate gland in men. It rarely moves further into the body. This infection is passed on through vaginal sex, though not through oral or anal sex, kissing, sharing cups or cutlery, or via toilet seats or towels. In rare cases, sharing sex toys can spread it, but this risk can be reduced by covering a sex toy with a condom.

Symptoms Trichomoniasis can be hard to diagnose as there may be no symptoms, and, if they do appear, it will be between four days and three weeks after infection. Women are more likely to have symptoms than men, and these may include soreness and itching around the vagina, an abnormal vaginal discharge (which may be smelly, particularly watery, foaming, and yellowish or greenish) and a burning sensation when urinating. Men usually have only slight bladder discomfort leading to pain after urination and/or ejaculation but may also have a thin white discharge from the penis. You can still pass on the infection even if you have no symptoms.

Treatment Trichomoniasis is very unlikely to clear up without treatment, and both partners need to take the antibiotic prescribed, even if one of them is symptomless. Avoid sexual intercourse until the infection is over.

YEAST INFECTIONS/THRUSH

Most women will experience vaginal thrush, at some time in their lives. The fungus that causes thrush – *Candida albicans* – lives on the skin in the mouth, gut and vagina, usually without causing any problem. Hormones in vaginal secretions and 'friendly' vaginal bacteria keep the fungus under control. Problems arise when the natural balance in the vagina is upset – when antibiotics are being taken, for example – and the fungus multiplies. Men can also suffer from yeast infections, though less commonly. Although it isn't an STI, thrush can be passed on during sex, even if the infected person has no symptoms. It is fairly harmless, but it can be uncomfortable and may recur.

Symptoms Itching, irritation and swelling of the vagina and area around it, sometimes accompanied by a creamy-white discharge. In men, the head of the penis and foreskin can become inflamed, and there can be pain while urinating and a smelly, lumpy discharge.

Treatment Anti-thrush cream, pessaries or tablets are usually prescribed which contain an anti-fungal agent. Although these are available over the counter, you should not treat yourself more than twice in six months with such products without visiting a doctor.

HONEYMOON CYSTITIS

This is actually not an STI. It is uncomfortable, but not dangerous. It often happens when a woman starts having sex with a new partner, hence the old expression 'honeymoon cystitis' from the days when girls had not had intercourse before their wedding night. Cystitis is inflammation of the bladder that occurs when bacteria is transferred from the anus to the urethra (which can happen during sex). Sometimes urinating immediately after sex can help to avoid this happening. And remember never to use the same condom for anal and vaginal sex. Cystitis can also develop if there is damage to or irritation of the urethra (perhaps as a result of vigorous and prolonged sexual intercourse).

Symptoms Symptoms include a discharge, a burning feeling when urinating, and a pulling sensation in the abdomen.

Treatment The symptoms of cystitis usually clear up without treatment within four to nine days. Some self-help treatments can ease discomfort, or your doctor may prescribe antibiotics.

SEXUAL HEALTH — WOMEN

Going for a gynaecological examination for the first time can feel a bit intimidating. After all, it involves a stranger examining the most intimate parts of your body. There's no need to go for an examination when your periods first start, although you might want to get help from a doctor if you are experiencing really painful cramps. And you definitely need to make an appointment at a doctor's surgery or sexual health clinic to sort out contraception for yourself or if you are worried that you might have a sexually transmitted infection of some sort. If you don't like the idea of being examined by a male doctor, ask if it is possible to see a woman.

Making an Appointment

When you speak to the receptionist, explain that this is your first appointment and that you would like to have enough time to deal with all your questions. Some health centres have special clinics for teenagers. Try to plan your first visit so that it doesn't coincide with your period. If you want to see someone quickly – because you need the morning-after pill, for example – make sure that you ask for an urgent appointment.

Getting Ready for Your Appointment

On the morning of your appointment, it's a good idea to have a shower. And if it's in the afternoon and you have time, you might like to freshen up again. No need to shave your pubic hair. For your examination, you will need to take off your underwear. Most people are not too keen on being half-naked in public: wearing a skirt or a long T-shirt and knee socks can help you to feel less exposed.

When You Get There

Once you have let the reception staff know who you are and the time of your appointment, you will probably be asked to wait until it's your turn to be seen. Before your examination a nurse or medical assistant may take your blood pressure. You may be asked when you started menstruating. Your height and weight will probably be noted, and you'll be asked whether you smoke and if you are taking any regular medication. Then it'll be time to see the doctor or health advisor.

The Talk

First the doctor or health advisor will probably have a short chat to learn a bit about you, and then you'll be asked why you have come for an appointment and whether you need some form of contraception. This conversation is completely confidential. Unless you choose to tell them, your parents will know nothing about it. If you don't understand something, feel free to ask for it to be explained.

The Examination

After you've spoken with the doctor, you'll be asked to go into a cubicle, or behind a screen to half-undress. If you're wearing socks you can keep them on. You may be asked to lie on a couch or to get on to a special chair with a footrest on each side. You'll be lying or sitting with your legs apart in front of the doctor. Keep in mind that the doctor examines lots of different women every day – for him or her, it's just a job. And it doesn't matter to the doctor whether or not you shave your pubic hair or have any intimate piercings.

First your skin will be checked for any abnormalities. It may or may not be necessary for you to have an internal examination. If you need one, the procedure is one that will become very familiar to you once you start being screened for cervical cancer by having smear tests (offered to women over the age of 25 in the UK). The doctor will gently insert a speculum into your vagina. A speculum is a long metal (or plastic) instrument with two arms that can be opened out slightly after it has been inserted so as to widen the vagina for a visual examination of the vaginal walls and cervix. Most women do not find this process painful (although the metal can feel a bit cold unless you have a particularly kindly doctor who has warmed it up a bit first!). The speculum will remain inside you for a few minutes if the doctor needs to take swabs to be sent to a laboratory. You can request a hand mirror (or bring your own) so that you can watch the examination for yourself: it's not often that you get the opportunity to see inside your own vagina. Lastly, the doctor may gently insert two fingers into the vagina while using the other hand to feel your bladder, uterus and ovaries through the abdominal wall and identify any lumps, fibroids or cysts.

If you've gone to a well woman clinic at a GP surgery or local hospital, you may be offered breast awareness advice (which is also available from many practice nurses in surgeries). If so, you'll need to remove your top so that the doctor or nurse can show you how to check for lumps in breasts. Then you'll be able to do this for yourself at home.

AND WHAT ABOUT BOYS?

Boys will need to pay a visit to a doctor, only if they have a specific problem with their sex organs. This could be if their foreskin is too tight, for example, or if they are experiencing pain in their testicles.

SEXUAL DYSFUNCTION

If you have problems with sex, you should first consult your GP. He or she will be able to talk to you about possible medical causes and suggest tests and/or medication. However, you need to bear in mind that most GPs have only about ten minutes to spend with each patient, and if medical causes are ruled out and you need an in-depth discussion about what is going wrong, you may need to go to a sex therapist. Your doctor should be able to advise you about the availability of sex therapy in your area, or see page 251 for organisations that can help. Unfortunately, consultations of this kind are not usually covered by the National Health Service in the UK or by health in-surance, so you are likely to have to pay your own fees.

Below, you'll find information about various kinds of sexual dysfunction, and the sorts of problem that sex therapists deal with all the time. Often all that is needed is a greater sense of awareness of your own body and needs (and those of your partner), and information about techniques.

IN WOMEN

Vaginismus

Vaginismus is a condition in which the muscles in a woman's pelvic floor are so contracted that it is almost impossible for a penis to enter the vagina. It could be done with a lot of force, probably causing pain in both partners, but this is not normal. In a woman suffering from vaginismus, the vagina is effectively sealed as a result of abnormally high muscle tension. There are various forms of the condition: in some cases it is impossible even to do a gynaecological examination; in others, an examination can be carried out without difficulty, but as soon as a penis approaches everything clamps shut. It often turns out that women are sealing themselves up for very good reasons. They may at some point have been sexually abused, for example. But not every woman with vaginismus has suffered sexual abuse. Fear can be a big part of the problem. Negative thoughts associated with having sex can make a person tense all over. Women with vaginismus tend to be either out of touch with their own sexuality or to have very negative feelings about it. For them, the vagina has nothing to do with enjoyment, and so has no pleasurable associations. Some women are unlucky enough to have grown up with no knowledge about their own sexuality, and no sexual sense of their bodies at all.

Dyspareunia

If a woman finds penetration painful, the condition is called dyspareunia. The pain may be experienced only when the penis is first entering the vagina, but it can also happen at any time after that. (Incidentally, the pain that some women experience the first time they have penetrative sex doesn't have anything to do with dyspareunia.)

You will usually be checked first for infections or endometriosis. If these results are clear, it's possible that the dyspareunia is being caused by: high levels of muscle tension, absence of arousal leading to dryness in the vagina, fear that intercourse will hurt, or other psychological issues including feelings of guilt or shame, negative thoughts, an upbringing in which sex was disapproved of, or having parents with strict and repressive moral codes.

Does It Hurt? Surveys have shown that around 20% of young women regularly find sexual intercourse painful, and many of them think that this is normal, or are afraid to talk about it. Nothing could be further from the truth: sex should certainly not hurt, and it ought to be fun! So if you are finding it painful, do get some help and advice before the problem becomes more deep-rooted.

Orgasm

What lies behind problems with achieving orgasm is almost always a combination of having missed out on learning about your own body and getting really stressed out about what isn't happening: *Oh no – not again. I just can't do it. There's no way I'm going to manage this! Come on, hurry up! He's not going to wait around for you.* But the truth is that every woman can learn to have an orgasm.

Lack of Sexual Appetite

We've already described how hormones contribute to lust. The optimal hormonal balance for a woman to feel at her most sexually aroused comes around only a few times each month. Men, on the other hand – at least until their mid-forties – are hormonally geared up much more of the time. In any case, though, if you have learned to be really aware of your libido and have also learned how to direct it, you can feel aroused even when the relevant hormones are at quite a low ebb.

Sex is hardly ever just about sex.
Shirley MacLaine

There are lots of other reasons why you may have no appetite for sex that have nothing to do with hormones. If you find that you often just don't feel like it, it may be that there is no real intimacy between you and your partner. If that's the case, the absence of desire can even be a good thing, as it may prompt you to confront and sort out what is not going so well in your relationship.

Anyone who has got to know themselves sexually can feel aroused on a daily basis whenever he or she feels like it. The truth is that sexual desire is not inborn, but learned. The better your experience of sex, the more of a taste you will develop for it. We talked earlier about how to nurture your own erotic personality when we were discussing masturbation (see pages 15-18). That's a great way to learn.

Sex is an emotion in motion.
Mae West

IN MEN

Premature Ejaculation

Coming too soon can be an issue at any age. It's pretty common for young men to come quite fast, but it doesn't have to be that way. When a young man masturbates, he can – to some extent at least – mimic what will happen when he has sex with a woman. The vagina is wet and warm, so he could use body oil on his hands, and he can practise moving his pelvis rather than his hand while breathing slowly and deeply. This will allow him to learn about his pelvic floor muscles and how to use them to delay getting to that point-of-no-return. If, by his twenties, a man is still battling with premature ejaculation, it would be a good idea for him to get some help.

Erectile Dysfunction (ED)

This is when a man finds it difficult to get an erection or to keep it going, meaning either that sexual intercourse never happens, or that it's possible only occasionally. It's more common for men to have difficulties with getting a hard-on as they grow older, but do consult a doctor, no matter what your age, if this is an issue for you. Surprisingly few men seek help for what can be a distressing condition. Performance anxiety, alcohol or drug abuse are all common reasons for erectile dysfunction among younger as well as older men. Underlying medical causes include diabetes, low hormone levels, high or low blood pressure, the effects of previous surgery or the side effects of a wide range of medications. If no underlying cause of erectile problems is discovered, a doctor will probably prescribe medication.

John Thomas says goodnight to Lady Jane, a little droopingly, but with a hopeful heart.
D.H. Lawrence, Lady Chatterley's Lover

The Elusive Stiffy Even young guys sometimes have a problem getting it up. It may be to do with nerves, worry about work or money, bereavement, or perhaps a few too many beers – resulting in a case of 'brewer's droop'. Don't get too worked up about this. Limp dicks happen. And it's worth knowing that a flaccid penis is just as sensitive as an erect one.

Viagra and Co

The notorious 'little blue pill', Viagra, and other similar drugs, are taken an hour before a man is planning to have sex. They work by boosting blood flow into the penis, and the effect lasts for around five hours. Even with Viagra, though, a man has to be feeling aroused. No excitement equals no erection, and that's why this drug sometimes doesn't work. A head full of negative thoughts will cancel out any effect the medication might have had. A lot of men end up consulting sex therapists either because Viagra hasn't worked or because they don't want to take any medication for their problem. Also, Viagra is not cheap. Often the best solution is to try a combination of advice from a sex therapist and some kind of potency drug.

Lack of Sexual Appetite

Exactly the same applies to men as to women. If you're finding sex unexciting, a bit of a strain or painful, you're not likely to have much appetite for it. If you're always worrying about coming too soon or losing your erection or doing something else wrong, it can really put you off. And then there are emotional issues. If something is wrong with a relationship, men and women alike can go off sex. Some illnesses, and often the medication that goes with them, can have a dampening effect on libido. A good example is clinical depression, which can lead to a serious dip in sexual desire, and the antidepressants used to treat it often have a similar effect.

And what is true for women also applies to men: the better and more sensitively a man knows his own body, and his partner's, the more important sex will be to him – even when he's preoccupied with problems at work, say, or feeling stressed for any other reason.

Dyspareunia

It's less common for men to experience pain during sex than it is for women. Causes include: a tight foreskin, a badly carried out circumcision, small lesions in the skin (which can result from friction during sex), infections and allergic reactions (to the latex in condoms, for example). Whatever the reason, if you find having sex painful, you should consult a doctor.

Other Issues

An obsession with pornography and internet-dependency and other issues can make trouble for you in your sex life, and they can all be treated. The important thing to remember is that if *you* feel something is wrong, you need to do something about it. If it's getting you down, causing problems in your relationship or leading you to hurt or do damage to other people, or even to break the law, then you need to take action and get help.

Because I feel as if I let it down. As if it needed something from me, I was its only hope, and now that hope is gone. What penis doesn't try to make you feel that way?
R.J. Silver

Marge, there's just too much pressure, what with my job, the kids, traffic sounds, political strife at home and abroad. But I promise you, the second all of these things go away, we'll have sex.
Homer, in The Simpsons

FLOATING FREE

THE SEXUAL UNIVERSE

IT'S A BIG WORLD OUT THERE

Sexuality spans a massive range of tastes and interests. Some people are happy having simple, uncomplicated sex. Others discover that it takes something extra for them to have a really good time. There's a vast range of sexual adventures to explore out there. As some of than can be quite risky, it's good for you always to be aware of your own needs, and completely clear about what you do and don't want for yourself. *Do I like the idea of doing that? Am I really enjoying this?* If you can honestly answer yes, then go ahead and have fun. If you aren't sure or you're really not happy with what's about to happen (or already happening), be brave and remove yourself from the situation before things go any further.

SEX ON A HIGH

Alcohol and hard drugs definitely change how people experience sex. Everything seems magnified and more intense. The senses become supercharged, and feelings are heightened, both positively and negatively. It's almost as though you're losing your sense of yourself, and pain thresholds tend to be much higher than normal – which is why the combination of sex and drugs can be dangerous.

Under the influence of drugs or alcohol, scruples and inhibitions vanish, things that you would normally baulk at don't worry you, and your ability to recognise danger is vastly reduced. None of this would be good at the best of times, but it's really not a great idea to expose yourself to such risks when you are just beginning to find out about your own sexuality. It's much better – and far more enjoyable – to be aware of everything that is happening and to experience it as fully as possible, rather than blacking out or being badly hung over the next day with no idea of what happened the night before. Savour every moment and treasure every memory: the stroking, the kisses, the touching.

I like to have a Martini,
Two at the very most,
After three I'm under the table
After four I'm under my host.
Dorothy Parker

Bye-bye Hard-on Alcohol definitely does not improve a man's ability to get an erection. The more alcohol he drinks, the more elusive a hard-on becomes. Alcohol causes blood vessels to widen, so more blood flows into the penis. That's good, but too much alcohol impairs the nervous system so that the mechanics of getting it up don't work so well: not good news for erections. Because your sexual reflexes will also have greatly diminished, the chances of reaching orgasm will be even slimmer.

Loss of Control

Someone who has drunk a lot of alcohol or taken hard drugs is unlikely to have much control over what happens to them. That can obviously be very risky, especially if you're among people you don't know very well.

Most people take drugs knowingly, but it can also happen involuntarily, if your drink is secretly spiked with knockout drops such as chloral hydrate, for example. The consequences can be serious, particularly if someone has taken advantage of you while you were out of it. If ever you wake up in the morning unable to remember much about what happened the night before and you know, or even suspect, that you have had sex, book an appointment with a doctor or at a sexual health clinic immediately. A blood test will establish whether drugs have entered your system, and a medical examination will reveal whether sexual intercourse has taken place. For girls, the morning-after pill will dramatically lessen the risk of pregnancy (see page 215). You should also be tested for STIs (sexually transmitted infections). If you believe you have been sexually assaulted, contact the police or a sexual assault referral centre. If, for whatever reason, you don't want to tell your parents what has happened, talk to another adult your trust, a teacher, for example, or use a helpline (see list of contacts on pages 250-251). Keep in mind that you can ask for a doctor to refer you to a counsellor or psychologist if an experience of this kind has left you in need of psychological support.

Going Public

When a love affair, or even a flirtation, comes to an end, things can turn nasty. It's not unusual for the person who feels they have been abandoned to deal with their anger and disappointment by taking revenge. Suddenly a torrent of offensive remarks and lies about you appears online, and the posts may well be accompanied by intimate photos or videos made when you were in bed together. It's a very mean thing for someone to do, but using social networking to harm or harass other people – cyberbullying – is unfortunately not uncommon.

She's gone. I am abused, and my relief must be to loathe her.
William Shakespeare, Othello

What can you do about it? First, ask your ex-partner to take down the posts. If that doesn't work, you could maybe talk to your parents about it, and perhaps your ex-partner's parents too. If that's impossible, talk to another adult you trust. At the same time, you should report offensive posts to the website administrator and apply for them to be removed. If none of these approaches works, the only other option open to you is to go to the police. Make sure that you take screenshots of the relevant webpages with you so that you can show exactly how you are being harassed.

Now back to the world of sex, where some things may seem a bit scary, and others truly weird. But maybe you'll find something unusual that catches your imagination. If so, take the time to find out a bit more about it.

KINKS

Sexual preferences vary enormously, and we're about to tell you a bit about what's out there. It can feel as though you are entering a parallel universe when you start discovering more about this, with territories you definitely cannot enter without a visa. Most of the practices described here qualify as unusual or special sexual interests, in other words, they are a long way from 'vanilla sex' (that is, straightforward sexual intercourse).

Some people have very specific fixations, in other words, fetishes. But how do different sexual tastes and cravings develop in the first place? Almost everyone has something they find really arousing and exciting. It might be the sight of leather trousers, high heels, designer stubble, or large or small boobs, or having a blowjob, or the thought of penetrating someone from behind. Anything can be a fetish. It seems highly likely that fixations like these are not inborn, but have been picked up along the way during a person's sexual development – in other words, they've been learned. Someone who is turned on by sweaty feet in red ballet pumps, for example, or who really goes for bodies tightly encased in rubber, has at some point learned to find these things exciting.

I have a thing for red-haired Irish boys, as we know.
Sandra Bullock

Most people have a range of fetishes, and it's great if you find things that work really well for you and make you feel sexy. It can get difficult, though, if someone is reliant on a single thing to get aroused, because then they've got to find a partner who shares their special interest. Going back to those red shoes, for example: there are likely to be very few women prepared to indulge a partner by coming up with a pair of sweaty feet to go with the pumps. If you're lucky enough to find someone who shares the same personal fetish, you're fine, but if you can't find anyone who has a taste for the only thing that turns you on, you may go off sex altogether. If you think that this may be true of you, it would be worth seeing a sex therapist, who is trained to help with issues like this. The range of things that make you feel sexy can be altered and broadened: everyone can learn new ways of becoming aroused.

Here are some of the more unusual interests that you may hear about or come across:

Urophilia or urolagnia
This is getting excited about urine – some people are turned on by peeing, others by being peed on (a so-called 'golden shower') or even

drinking their partner's urine. In some cases, just the smell of urine is enough to excite someone.

Coprophilia

Getting excited by the sight, touch or smell of faeces (shit), or by the process of defecation – the sensation of faeces passing through the anus.

Infantilism

Not to be confused with paedophilia (wanting to commit sexual acts with a child), infantilism is an exclusively adult activity and includes the desire to treated, some of the time, like a small child or baby. This often involves wearing nappies and having them changed, and being caressed as a child would be by its parents.

Feederism

Feederism has to do with getting sexual pleasure from eating (typically very large amounts of food) and is often a solitary activity. It seems to be the feeling of fullness and the pressure on internal organs that are the turn-on. Some people who do this can reach orgasm without even being touched.

BDSM

A perhaps surprisingly large minority of sexually active people are into one or more of the practices that go under the heading BDSM. Coined in the late 1960s, BDSM is usually taken to mean Bondage, Discipline, Sadism and Masochism (using, for example, chains, ropes, disciplining, domination and subjugation). Often abbreviated to S&M, BDSM covers a whole range of sexual behaviour, including, among other things, domination and submission, punishment games, pleasure heightened by pain, and bondage.

The crucial ground-rules for S&M are that it should be voluntary and consensual (i.e. both partners have agreed to it), that both people know exactly what is going to happen and that it happens within safe limits. What all of these practices have in common is that you are agreeing to play games during which power is shared out very unequally.

It's often thought that S&M is a very marginal activity, and that it's evil, dirty or perverse. People think of chains, beatings, PVC and leather, handcuffs, shackles and whips. You definitely have to do some research into this kind of sexuality to understand its appeal and what it involves. There are countless variations on the theme, but essential to all of them is a high level of mutual trust in those taking part.

S&M is a consensual game of role-playing in which one partner takes a dominant role, the other a submissive one. The submissive partner derives pleasure from putting him or herself entirely in the hands of the dominant partner. Obviously, complete trust in your partner is crucial. If there is even a suspicion that the dominant partner might overstep the boundaries you have set together, S&M should be out of the question. With S&M sex, it's important that everything is thoroughly discussed beforehand. And agreeing on a code for 'stop' is essential so that a single word from the submissive partner will guarantee that the session or activity stops instantly. Nothing more can happen.

Where pain is involved, the desired effect results from pain triggering the production of certain hormones and neurotransmitters to produce a kind of sensual trance. This starts very slowly and gradually builds.

Using whips, chains, tying a person up, and so on, are skilled activities, and it takes time to learn how to do them properly. The first law of the S&M scene is safety. There are, for example, such things as beginners' whips that are designed not to do too much damage. And you need to be trained in how to apply chains so that there is no risk of interrupting the blood supply to any part of the body. Ideally, everything should happen in a highly controlled way with the dominant partner knowing precisely what the boundaries are. That way both partners will have a good time.

Sticks and stones may break my bones
But chains and whips excite me.
Rhianna, S&M

Most young people are not particularly interested in S&M. But many people who would never want to feel pain still like to relinquish a bit of control and be told what to do by the other person from time to time. So they might sometimes want their partner to make the decisions about how exactly they will have sex, or enjoy being given instructions, or like being held down by their hands or perhaps loosely tied up. Giving up some control temporarily – as long as this is completely voluntary – can be sexy. It's all about slipping in and out of different roles, and it can be very exciting.

The Play Instinct Many of the more extreme attraction codes (patterns of stimulation) play on the emotions. In other words, the driver of the excitement is emotional rather than physical. For connoisseurs of S&M, orgasm, for example, is often not the point – it's the role-playing and the emotional excitement that matter. Some couples stay in character all the time, playing out their chosen roles 24/7.

Group Sex

Sex with more than one other person at a time. It could be a threesome, or it might involve more people.

Swingers Clubs

You can visit a swingers club on your own or with your partner. There's usually a bar and there'll be playrooms – sometimes equipped with various kinds of kit such as very large beds, swings hanging from the ceiling, and even some S&M items. You can have sex with your partner, or watch other people having sex, or swap partners, maybe having sex with several people at a time or with one after another.

If you go to a swingers club you need to be very clear about your own boundaries and able to recognise those of other people. This is not a place where you can just do whatever you want. What is expected is respectful interaction. You need to find out about each club's rules, and be aware that if you abuse them, you'll be thrown out. In most countries, you have to be at least 18 to get into a swingers club.

Brothels

A brothel is a place where you pay to have sex with someone. Usually, it's men buying sex with women – you might want to ask yourself why that should be. Surveys show that sex workers frequently come from difficult backgrounds and often have a history of being abused or even raped. Some need the money to fund a drug habit or to pay a pimp (who will keep most of the earnings for himself). Others are illegal immigrants lured from abroad by people traffickers. Their passports are taken from them and they are forced to work against their will. Some women, however, freely decide to earn their living by selling their sexual services.

In some countries, prostitution has been made illegal. In Sweden, for example, as the result of a groundbreaking law that came into force in 1999, anyone buying sexual services risks a fine or up to six months in prison. By contrast with legislation in other countries, Swedish law makes the client rather than the sex worker culpable. The ban on prostitution in Sweden is based on the belief that this business is incompatible with respect for women.

Some independent sex workers claim that they enjoy their work and insist that they are not exploited. It is hard to make any judgement about individual cases. What persuades or drives sex workers to ply their trade remains a complicated issue.

Planet Porn

The people who live on this planet often look a bit different. The men have enormous dicks and the women unnaturally large, gravity-defying boobs.

There are vast numbers of porn films, the majority made to appeal to men. It is important to be clear that sexuality as shown in porn films usually has nothing to do with reality. In fact, much of what you will see is either physically impossible or just doesn't happen in real life. Be under no illusions: elaborate preparations will have been made before the cameras roll. Anal muscles will have been thoroughly stretched so that the anal sex scenes will (literally) go smoothly. Vast quantities of fake semen will have been manufactured, ready to gush out everywhere.

There are various styles of porn film, including some produced to look like home movies, others featuring a range of couples – man and woman, man and man, woman and woman, and 'full bush' movies starring performers with unshaven pubic hair.

And then there are all the fetishes and kinks that we've already referred to, plus many others, including a particular form of anal-oral sex called 'rimming'. This involves using the tongue to lick or kiss a partner's anus (the anal rim) before penetration of the anus with the tongue. Or there is fisting: instead of a penis, not just a finger but a whole fist is inserted into the vagina or the anus. NB: this technique has to be used with great care because of the risk of injury.

My reaction to porno films is as follows: after the first ten minutes I want to go home and screw. After the first twenty minutes I never want to screw again as long as I live. *Erica Jong*

Sex Toys

Many people regard a selection of sex toys in their bedside table as basic equipment. Others have no interest in them or even find them disgusting. There are many options, including edible underwear, masks, chambermaid costumes, furry handcuffs, chocolate body paint (to smear over the body and then lick off), to name but a few.

Dildos

Dildos are sex toys in the shape of a penis. They can be made out of rubber, plastic, silicone, or even glass, ceramic, wood, steel or bone and are available in an infinite variety of shapes and colours including little mice, dolphins or an S-shaped dildo that is good for massaging the female prostate (G-zone). Dildos can be used vaginally or anally. Some models have fancy little attachments designed to stimulate the clitoris during penetration. You can use a dildo on your own, or as a couple. Some (called vibrators) have a vibrating function, with different settings for various rhythms and strengths of vibration that can cause a very pleasurable sensation on the clitoris or penis. Don't overuse them, though, or you may start to find it hard to come without vibration. A dildo can feel really cold, so make sure you warm it up in some water before you insert it. And if you decide to find a new use for cucumbers or other vegetables, just put a condom over them first. (It's perhaps worth investing in the vegetable-shaped dildos made out of silicone that are available.) Dildos can be helpful for women who want to investigate how to feel more inside their vagina during sex with a man. If you're using one for this reason, switch off the vibration – your partner's penis won't be doing much buzzing during intercourse.

Dildos made specifically for rectal use are called anal plugs or butt plugs and are shaped so that they are easy to get out again. The anal sphincter – the muscles round the anus – tends to suck things up inside. So make sure you don't insert anything into your own anus, or anyone else's, that might disappear. And please don't use dildos longer than a maximum of 15 cm, as the rectum is only 15 to 25 cm long. Beyond it is a turn in the passage that leads to the bowel, and you can cause a nasty injury if you push too long an object inside. Rectal dildos can be used to massage a man's prostate from the inside, producing a super-charged orgasm.

Sex Games

Among other games, there are, for example, sets of dice that have different instructions on each face telling you where to have sex and in what position. Games like this can really stoke up sexual excitement. And there are various board games that almost guarantee a rise in the sexual temperature and culminate in sexual intercourse. They're great for exploring new ways of having sex.

Love Swing/Sex Swing

This is for those who want to try something a little more advanced. It's a kind of harness, often with a hammock-like component that hangs from the ceiling. One person is suspended in it, while the other stands on the ground moving his or her partner around and pleasuring them. If you're interested in acquiring one of these, buy it from a sex shop. Don't attempt to make your own.

Strap-on

A strap-on is a belt incorporating an artificial penis (usually made of rubber) that allows a woman to penetrate her partner, whether male or female.

Cock Rings or Penis Rings

Also known as erection rings or tension rings, these can be made out of silicone, metal, rubber or leather. They are designed to intensify erections and make them last longer (by slowing down the flow of blood out of the erectile tissue). They are usually placed around the base of the penis, though some styles can be used around the scrotum as well. (A ring used around the scrotum alone is sometimes called a testicle cuff.) Others are shaped so as to simultaneously stimulate the clitoris during sex.

Dildos Ancient and Modern The world's oldest known dildo – a 28,000-year-old stone phallus, 20 cm long – was found in a cave near Ulm, Germany, in 2005. The Ancient Egyptians made dildos from clay; the Chinese had lacquered wood and porcelain versions. Later they were made from leather, wood, wax and glass. They were used vaginally as well as anally – sometimes simultaneously. An Ancient Greek vase painting shows a double-ended dildo. The word 'dildo' was first used in English in an erotic poem by Thomas Nashe in the 1590s and was mentioned in 17th-century plays by Ben Jonson and William Shakespeare.

In Europe an estimated 25% to 50% of women own one or more dildos and/or vibrators. In the USA, until recently, a number of Southern and Midwestern states banned the sale of dildos, either specifically or through laws regulating 'obscene devices', and as late as 2007, a Federal Appeals Court upheld Alabama's law prohibiting the sale of sex toys.

Unsurprisingly, vibrators first appeared after the arrival of electricity. They were initially developed not to enhance or increase sexual arousal, but to treat hysteria in women. For hundreds of years, but especially in the late 19th and early 20th centuries, hysteria was a common medical diagnosis, made exclusively in women, and numerous medical papers were written on the subject. Women with a vast range of different symptoms were packed off to doctors and diagnosed as suffering from the condition.

The treatment of hysteria (often thought to be linked to sexual problems, including not wanting to have sex) was as crazy as its diagnosis: the patient would be asked to sit in a kind of gynae-cological chair. The lower half of her body would be naked and covered with a towel. Beneath this, the doctor would massage her clitoris and vulva (so-called 'vaginal massage') until a 'paroxysm' (or orgasm) was produced. This 'relaxation therapy' was supposed to reduce hysterical attacks. Performing this service manually in doctors' offices was time-intensive, and soon mechanical vibrators became available, allowing the treatments to be administered faster. The first machines were equipped with huge generators, suitable only to be used in medical practices. But from the 1900s, vibrators for home use became available, allowing women to treat(!) themselves. No mention of any sexual application was made in sales materials, however. Vibrators were sold as tools for massaging the skin and for regulating menstruation. As a result, by an impressive feat of marketing, they were promoted as helping married women to retain their youthful good looks.

Astonishingly, the diagnosis of hysteria was not abandoned until the early 1950s.

Latex Sheets

To experience a different kind of sensuality, you could try latex sheets. If this makes you think of S&M, you're not far wrong, but they have other uses too. Latex sheets are great when you want to have sex using loads of body oil. Sex when you're covered in oil is a new experience, because you're so slippery that you have to hold on to each other more. Your whole body will move differently, and even the way it responds to touch will be changed. You'll experience a fantastic sense of intimacy, and there'll be a lot of laughter. If you don't want things to get quite so slippery, or for a cheaper alternative, you can use a couple of large handtowels. It's not quite the same experience but it can still be a lot of fun. But beware if you are using condoms: oil and oil-based products like petroleum jelly react with latex, quickly weakening it, so condoms are likely to break. Make sure you use a silicone- or water-based lubricating gel instead.

Tantric Sex

If you go for a tantric massage, your naked body will, over the course of a couple of hours, be stroked, squeezed, kneaded and caressed from head to foot with feathers, warmed stones, cloths, fur or even with the masseur's entire body. Most people have never experienced anything like the extraordinary range of sensations produced by this kind of massage, which has a profoundly sensual effect, giving you a profound awareness and sense of your own body. You can go for tantric massage either alone or with a partner. Couples can then try experimenting at home with the techniques they have learned.

There are many styles of tantric sex, but they all originate in India as part of a mystical philosophy. Tantric sex is a slow, sustained form of intercourse during which the aim is to allow sexual energy to build very gradually so that, slowly, the entire body becomes involved. The idea is for multiple channels to be opened up throughout the body, for all the senses to be engaged simultaneously and for close connections to be created between an individual's body and feelings.

Although it can take a bit of an effort to allow yourself to let go enough to get the best out of the experience, it can be enormously rewarding. Sexual sensation overtakes more and more of the body, becoming increasingly intense, and the climax, when it finally comes, is a massive, overwhelming wave of pleasure. Tantric sex could be described as the highest level of advanced sexual practice.

APPENDIX

THE AUTHORS

Born in Viborg, Denmark in 1964, Ann-Marlene Henning studied neuropsychology in Hamburg, followed by sexology in Denmark and Switzerland. She now has her own psychotherapy practice in Hamburg where she offers couples therapy and sex therapy using the Sexocorporel method which promotes sexual pleasure as a central goal of sex counselling.

Tina Bremer-Olszewski, born in Stade, Germany, in 1973, is a freelance journalist. After doing cultural studies at the university of Hildesheim, she became a journalist. She contributes to various national print and online publications in Germany. For more than ten years, she was also a volunteer youth worker, acting, among other things, as a mentor for young people attending summer camps.

THE PHOTOGRAPHER

The photographs in this book were made by Heji Shin, who works internationally doing documentary work, including art and fashion photography. Born in Seoul, South Korea, in 1976, she studied in Hamburg and now divides her time between Berlin and New York. She contributes regularly to magazines such as *Interview, Wire, 032c* and *Zeit Magazin*, as well as participating in both group and solo exhibitions.

ABOUT THIS BOOK

This book draws on a number of fundmental principles that originate in the Sexocorporell concept developed in Canada in the 1960s by Professor Jean-Yves Desjardins and his colleagues. Courses in the Sexocorporell method are now available in France, Germany, Austria and Switzerland. At its core is the recognition that while a sexual reflex in the genitals is inborn, the ability to enjoy sex, whether alone or as a couple, is not. How we treat our bodies and look after them, how we move and breathe, and how much we have learned about our own antaomies and sexuality all has a decisive effect on our moods and emotions. That is true in general, but it is particularly true when it comes to sex. The Sexocorporell approach encourages people to unlock their erotic potential, both physical and emotional, and to explore and develop it. Some of these ideas can be found in this book. More information is available from the Institut Sexocoporel International (www.sexocorporel.com).

ACKNOWLEDGEMENTS

We would particularly like to thank: Johanna von Rauch, Till Tolkemitt, Andreas Wellnitz, Heji Shin, Dr Karoline Bischof, Ida Thiemann, Florentine Draeger, and our friends and families. Without your work, expertise, creativity, patience, and willingness to provide information and support, this book would not be what it is.

Creating the English edition of the book required a further layer of editorial work, and we are grateful to the following people for their cooperation and generosity in sharing knowledge, expertise and information: Dr Arif Aslam, Dr Mandy Claiden, Lucy Emmerson of the Sex Education Forum, Alison Hadley OBE of the Teenage Pregnancy Information Exchange, Natika Halil of the Family Planning Association, Joseph Hancock of the Research Communications Office for the Health Behaviour in School-aged Children WHO Collaborative Cross-National Study, Rachel Hayton, Maria del Mar Hollis, Dr Caroline Owen, and Dr David Regis of the Schools and Students Health Education Unit, Exeter.

USEFUL WEBSITES

www.childline.org.uk   Free and confidential source of support and advice for young people of all ages in distress or danger. Telephone helpline (0800 1111), email via the website, or chat online available 24 hours a day. Website provides information about sex, relationships, contraception, sexually transmitted infections, pregnancy, abortion, adoption and relationship abuse.

www.brook.org.uk   Confidential advice on sexual health, pregnancy and contraception for young people under 25. Free telephone helpline 0808 802 1234, open Monday-Friday 9am-6pm (closed on Thursdays 2pm-3.30pm).

www.nhs.co.uk/livewell/sexandyoungpeople   Information for young people on many topics including sexual health, same-sex relationships, contraception, pregnancy, abortion and where to find your local sexual health clinic. Advice for girls: **www.nhs.uk/livewell/teengirls**; advice for boys: **www.nhs.uk/livewell/teenboys**.

www.fpa.org.uk   Provides information and advice aimed at allowing everyone to make informed choices about sex, relationships and reproduction, including information about contraceptive methods, sexually transmitted infections, pregnancy and abortion.

www.stonewall.org.uk   Provides information and support for lesbians, gay men and bisexual people. Their *Education for All* campaign tackles homophobia and homophobic bullying in schools in the UK.

www.lgbtyouth.org.uk   Information and support for lesbian, gay, bisexual and transgender young people in Scotland.

www.mermaids.org.uk   Information and telephone helpline (020 8123 4819) for children and teenagers with gender identity issues and their families.

www.eachaction.org.uk   Information about homophobia and transphobia, and a telephone helpline for young people who are experiencing homophobic or transphobic bullying (0808 1000 143).

www.schools-out.org.uk   Works towards equality in education for lesbian, gay, bisexual and trans people. Find out more about your rights at school with the Schools Out student toolkit.

www.thinkuknow.co.uk   Offers information to young people on sex, relationships and the internet, providing up-to-date, practical and safe advice. If you are worried about the behaviour of another adult online, visit thinkuknow to make a report.

www.thehideout.org.uk   Website for young people up to the age of 21 where they can find information about relationship abuse and where to get help.

www.heartprogramme.org   EU-funded programme with anonymous, confidential helpline supplied by Childline (0800 1111, 24 hours) offering help and advice to young people on how to have healthy relationships with boy or girl friends, and particularly on how to avoid feeling pressurised into doing something you don't want to do.

www.thisisabuse.direct.gov.uk   Abuse is not normal and never OK. If you are feeling scared, intimidated or controlled, it's possible you are in an abusive relationship. Find out where you can get help on this website.

www.rapecrisis.org.uk   Rape Crisis Centres offers a range of services for women and girls who have been raped or experienced another form of sexual violence, including contact details for your nearest Rape Crisis Centre. Some centres also deal with boys. Telephone helpline 0808 802 9999, 12pm-2.30pm and 7pm-9.30pm.

www.respectphoneline.org.uk   Respect runs support services and programmes for men and women who inflict violence in relationships. Telephone helpline 0808 802 4040 open Monday to Friday 9am-5pm.

www.childnet.com   Childnet International works with other organisations to help children and young adults use the internet safely. For tips on making smart decisions over social networking, visit kidsmart.org.uk.

www.tht.org.uk   The Terrence Higgins Trust offers help and support including advice on HIV testing, treatment and health management. Also provides HIV counselling and practical avice to those worried that they may have contracted the disease. Telephone helpline: 0808 802 1221.

www.nspcc.org.uk   Free 24-hour helpline – 0800 028 3550 – for anyone concerned that a child is at risk of female genital mutilation (FGM), and for advice, information or support.

FURTHER READING & SOURCES

Daniel G. Amen and Patrick Lawlor, *Sex on the Brain*, 2007

Margot Anand, *The New Art of Sexual Ecstasy*, 2009

Stephanie Brill & Rachel Pepper, *The Transgender Child: A Handbook for Families and Professionals*, 2008

Louann Brizendine, *The Female Brain*, 2008

Louann Brizendine, *The Male Brain*, 2011

David Deida, *The Way of the Superior Man*, 2004

Rhonda Findling, *Don't Call That Man: A Survival Guide to Letting Go*, 2000

Cordelia Fine, *Delusions of Gender: The Real Science behind Sex Differences*, 2011

Helen Fisher, *Anatomy of Love: A Natural History of Mating, Marriage and Why We Stray*, 1995

Helen Fisher, *Why We Love: The Nature and Chemistry of Romantic Love*, 2005

Eric Franklin, *Pelvic Power: Mind/Body Exercises for Strength, Flexibility, Posture and Balance for Men and Women*, 2003

Suzi Godson & Mel Agace, *The Sex Book*, 2002

John Gray, *Men Are from Mars, Women from Venus*, 2002

John Gray, *Mars and Venus in the Bedroom: A Guide to Lasting Romance and Passion*, 2003

Dennis Greenberger & Christine A. Padesky, *Mind Over Mood*, 1995

Stephan B. Poulter, *Your Ex-Faktor: Overcome Heartbreak and Build a Better Life*, 2010

Kenneth Purvis, *The Male Sexual Machine*, 1992, 2002

Mary Roach, *Bonk: The Curious Coupling of Sex and Science*, 2009

Jenni Russell, *Pelvic Floor Secrets*, 2013

David Schnarch, *Intimacy and Desire*, 2009

Deborah Sundahl, *Female Ejaculation and the G-Spot*, 2004

Rachel Swift, *How to Have an Orgasm as Often as You Want*, 2005

INFOGRAPHICS

15-year-olds who have had sex pp.28-29
Source: C. Currie *et al.* eds. *Social determinants of health and well-being among young people. Health Behaviour in School-aged Children (HBSC)*: international report from the 2009/2010 survey, Copenhagen, WHO Regional Office for Europe, 2012

Who or what is your main source of information about sex?/ What would you prefer to be your main source of information about sex? pp.32-33
Source: data drawn from the work of SHEU (the Schools and Students Health Education Unit, Exeter) and reproduced with their permission from *Young People into 2013*.
www.sheu.org.uk

From what age is it legal to have sex? pp.34-35
Source: AVERT

Porn and Reality p.47
Source: Mascotte Film AG

Tattoos p.85
Source: Arif Aslam and Caroline M. Owen, survey data reported in 'Fashions Change but Tattoos Are Forever', *British Journal of Dermatology*, 2013

Active/Passive, One Partner/Several Partners p.97
Independent research

Circles of Love p.106
Independent research

Sex and relationship education p.111
Source: Sex Education Forum

Slang in various languages for vagina, breasts, penis, testicles pp.120-121 and 142-143
Source: Kauderwelsch Dictionaries (Reise Know-How Verlag) and independent research

Hair removal pp.124-125
Source: Professor Dr Elmar Brähler, *Survey of the Prevalence of Tattooing, Piercing and Depilation in Germany (Verbreitung*

von Tätowierungen, Piercing und Körperhaarentfernung in Deutschland), 2009

What happens after fertilisation? pp.130-131
Independent research

Male and female sex organs pp.132-133
independent research

Sex positions pp.151-152
independent research

Condom use by 15-year-olds internationally p.211
Source: C. Currie *et al.* eds. *Social determinants of health and well-being among young people. Health Behaviour in School-aged Children (HBSC)*: international report from the 2009/2010 survey, Copenhagen, WHO Regional Office for Europe, 2012

Sexual health service rights p.215
Source: Sex Education Forum

Success rates of different methods of contraception pp.216-217
Source: Pearl Index and pro familia/BZgA

Teenage pregnancy p.220
Sources: Office of National Statistics and Ipsos Mori poll conducted with Royal Statistical Society and King's College, London

HIV diagnoses in Europe p.222
Source: WHO Europe
Western Europe: Austria, Belgium, Denmark, Finland, France, Germany, Greece, Iceland, Ireland, Italy, Luxembourg, Malta, Netherlands, Norway, Portugal, Spain, Sweden, UK
Central Europe: Bulgaria, Croatia, Czech Republic, Hungary, Poland, Romania, Serbia, Slovakia, Slovenia, Turkey
Eastern Europe: Armenia, Azerbaijan, Belarus, Estonia, Georgia, Kazakhstan, Kyrgyzstan, Latvia, Lithuania, Republic of Moldova, Russian Federation, Tajikistan, Ukraine, Uzbekistan

INDEX